Nelson *Mathematics* 4

Teacher's Resource

Chapter 2: Numeration

Series Authors and Senior Consultants
Mary Lou Kestell • Marian Small

Senior Authors
Heather Kelleher • Kathy Kubota-Zarivnij • Pat Milot
Betty Morris • Doug Super

Teacher's Resource Chapter Author
Wendy Klassen

Assessment Consultant
Damian Cooper

THOMSON
NELSON

Australia   Canada   Mexico   Singapore   Spain   United Kingdom   United States

THOMSON

NELSON

Nelson Mathematics 4
Teacher's Resource

Series Authors and
Senior Consultants
Mary Lou Kestell, Marian Small

Senior Authors
Heather Kelleher,
Kathy Kubota-Zarivnij, Pat Milot,
Betty Morris, Doug Super

Authors
Carol Brydon, Anne Cirillo,
Andrea Dickson, Roz Doctorow,
Wendy Dowling, Catharine Gilmour,
Elizabeth Grill-Donovan,
Jack Hope, Wendy Klassen,
Kathy Kubota-Zarivnij,
David Leach, Pat Margerm,
Gail May, Pat Milot,
Scott Sincerbox, Marian Small,
Mary Steele, Susan Stuart,
Debbie Sturgeon, Rosita Tseng Tam

Assessment Consultant
Damian Cooper

Director of Publishing
David Steele

Publisher, Mathematics
Beverley Buxton

Senior Program Manager
Shirley Barrett

Teacher's Resource
Program Managers
Alan Simpson
David Spiegel

Developmental Editors
Janice Barr
Julie Bedford
Jenna Dunlop
James Gladstone
Adrienne Mason
Margaret McClintock
Janice Nixon
Frances Purslow
Elizabeth Salomons
Tom Shields
Alan Simpson
Michael Tabor

Editorial Assistant
Christi Davis

Executive Managing Editor,
Development & Testing
Cheryl Turner

Executive Managing Editor,
Production
Nicola Balfour

Production Editor
Lu Cormier

Copy Editor
Kathryn Dean

Production Coordinator
Franca Mandarino

Manufacturing Coordinator
Sharon Latta Paterson

Creative Director
Angela Cluer

Art Director
Ken Phipps

Art Management
ArtPlus Ltd., Suzanne Peden

Illustrators
ArtPlus Ltd.

Interior and Cover Design
Suzanne Peden

Cover Image
Corbin/Magna

ArtPlus Ltd. Production
Coordinator
Dana Lloyd

Composition
Alicia Countryman/ArtPlus Ltd.

Photo Research and
Permissions
Vicki Gould

Printer
Webcom

National Library of Canada
Cataloguing in Publication

Nelson mathematics 4.
Teacher's resource /
Mary Lou Kestell ... [et al.].

ISBN 0-17-620183-1

1. Mathematics—Study and
teaching (Elementary)
I. Kestell, Mary Lou
II. Title: Nelson mathematics four.

QA135.6.N444 2003 Suppl. 3
510   C2003-904835-7

Contents

OVERVIEW

Introduction 1
Curriculum Across Grades 3 to 5: Numeration 2
Math Background: Research and Important Issues 3
Planning for Instruction 3
    Problem Solving 3
    Connections to Literature 3
    Connections to Other Math Strands 3
    Connections to Other Curricula 3
    Connections to Home and Community 3
    Chapter 2 Planning Chart 4
Planning for Assessment 6
    Chapter 2 Assessment Chart 7
Reading Strategies 8

TEACHING NOTES

Chapter Opener 9
Getting Started: Modelling Numbers 10
Lesson 1: Place Value 13
Lesson 2: Expanded Form 17
Lesson 3: Comparing and Ordering Numbers 21
Lesson 4: Exploring 10 000 25
    Mental Math: Adding Tens, Hundreds, and Thousands 28
    Lesson 5: Multiplying by 10, 100, and 1000 29
    Mid-Chapter Review 33
    Math Game: Getting to 10 000 36
    Lesson 6: Rounding to the Nearest 10, 100, or 1000 . 37
    Lesson 7: Communicate About Ordering Numbers . . 41
    Lesson 8: Counting Money Collections 45
    Skills Bank 49
    Problem Bank 51
    Chapter Review 52
    Chapter Task 56

CHAPTER 2 BLACKLINE MASTERS

Family Newsletter 58
Mental Math 59
Chapter 2 Test 61
Chapter 2 Task 63
Scaffolding for Getting Started Activity 65
Scaffolding for Do You Remember? 66
Scaffolding for Lesson 3 67
Scaffolding for Lesson 6 68
Chapter 2 Answers (Problems of the Week, Mental Math,
    Chapter Test) 69
From Multi-Chapter Masters Booklet
Initial Assessment Summary (Tool 1) 1
What to Look For When Assessing Student Achievement
    (Tool 2) 2
Coaching Students Towards Success (Tool 3) 3
Conducting In-Class Student Interviews 4
Student Interview Form (with prompts) (Tool 4) 5
Student Interview Form (without prompts) (Tool 5) . . 6
Problem Solving Rubric (Tool 6) 7
Understanding of Concepts Rubric (Tool 7) 8
Application of Procedures Rubric (Tool 8) 9
Communication Rubric (Tool 9) 10
Using the Assessment of Learning Summary—
    Individual Student 11
Assessment of Learning Summary—Individual Student
    (Tool 10) 12
Using the Assessment of Learning Summary—Class
    by Strand 13
Assessment of Learning Summary—Class by Strand
    (Tool 11) 14
Play Money 1 27
Play Money 2 28
Play Money 3 29
Number Lines 32
Base Ten Blocks 33-35
Place Value Mat: Thousands, Hundreds,
    Tens, Ones 36
Place Value Mat: Hundreds, Tens, Ones 37

Introduction

This chapter extends students' understanding of the place value system from 3-digit numbers (emphasized in Grade 3) to 4-digit numbers. Students will continue to consider
- how to read a numeral
- how the size of a number relates to its representation
- how to represent an amount using numbers, words, or concrete materials in different ways

    The number 10 000 is also introduced in the context of patterns.

    This chapter also connects computation to students' understanding of the place value system. Students are taught

that multiplication by 10, 100, or 1000 is based on how we write numbers; this extends previous work where calculations involving adding 10, 100, or 1000 were also related to our numeration system.

Communication Focus: Explaining Thinking
Lesson 7 provides another opportunity for students to consider how clearly and completely they explain their thinking.

Curriculum Across Grades 3 to 5: Numeration

All the Grade 4 expectations listed below are covered in this chapter.
When the expectation is a focus of the lesson, the lesson number is indicated in brackets.

Grade 3	Grade 4	Grade 5
Overall Expectations: • represent whole numbers using concrete materials, drawings, numerals, and number words • compare and order whole numbers using concrete materials, drawings, and ordinals • solve problems and describe and explain the variety of strategies used	**Overall Expectations:** • compare and order whole numbers using concrete materials and drawings (**3, 4 7**) • solve problems involving whole numbers, and describe and explain the variety of strategies used (**1, 3**)	**Overall Expectations:** • compare, order, and represent whole numbers, using concrete materials and drawings • understand the significance of numbers within the surrounding environment
Specific Expectations: **Understanding Number** • read and print numerals from 0 to 1000 • read and print number words to one hundred • use ordinal numbers to hundredth • identify and describe numbers to 1000 in real-life situations to develop a sense of number (e.g., tell how high a stack of 1000 pennies would be) • model numbers grouped in hundreds, tens, and ones and use zero as a place holder • use a calculator to examine number relationships and the effect of repeated operations on numbers (e.g., explore the pattern created in the units column when 9 is repeatedly added to a number) • compare and order whole numbers using concrete materials, drawings, and ordinals • solve problems and describe and explain the variety of strategies **Units of Measure** • read and write money amounts using two forms of notation (89¢ and $0.89) • estimate, count, and record the value up to $10 of a collection of coins and bills • demonstrate the relationship among all coins and bills up to $100	**Specific Expectations:** **Understanding Number** • recognize and read numbers to 10 000 (**1, 2, 4**) • read and write whole numbers to 10 000 in standard, expanded, and written forms (**2**) • represent the place value of whole numbers to 10 000 using concrete materials, drawings, and symbols (**1, 2, 3, 4**) • compare and order whole numbers to 10 000 using concrete materials, drawings, and symbols (**1, 2, 3, 7**) • multiply whole numbers by 10, 100, and 1000 (**5**) • represent and explain number concepts and procedures (**4, 5, 6, 7**) • identify the use of numbers in various careers (**2**) • identify and appreciate the use of numbers in the media (**3, 6**) **Applications** • explain their thinking when solving problems involving whole numbers (**7**) **Units of Measure** • read and write money values to $50 (**8**) • estimate the amount of money in collections of coins and bills to $50, and count to determine the total value (**8**)	**Specific Expectations:** **Understanding Number** • recognize and read numbers to 100 000 • read and write whole numbers to 100 000 in standard, expanded, and written forms (e.g., 82 011 = 80 000 + 2000 + 10 + 1 = eighty-two thousand eleven) • identify and investigate the use of number in various careers • identify and interpret the use of numbers in the media • compare, order, and represent the place value of whole numbers to 100 000 using concrete materials, drawings, and symbols • explain their thinking when solving problems involving whole numbers • explain processes and solutions with whole numbers using mathematical language **Units of Measure** • read and write money values to $1000 • estimate the amount of money in collections of coins and bills to $1000, and count to determine the total value

Math Background: Research and Important Issues

Place Value System: This chapter extends students' familiarity with 3-digit numbers to numbers up to and including 10 000; it also builds on their previous experience with the principle that as soon as you have 10 of one grouping, you can trade them for one of the next size.

Expressing Numbers in Different Ways: Not only is it important for students to be confident in reading, writing, and representing numbers, but it is critical that they can rename numbers in a variety of ways. This flexibility will enhance students' success with the various number operations. Renaming should continue to be supported by the use of concrete materials at this level, whether they are base ten blocks on a place value chart; pennies, dimes, and loonies; or other physical models.

Calculations Linked to the Place Value System: The nature of our place value system makes certain calculations particularly simple, whether adding 10, 100, 1000 or multiplying by 10, 100 or 1000. For example, to add 1000, you only need to add 1 to the thousands digit. To multiply by 100, you need to enlarge each part of a number by a factor of 100, so ones become hundreds, tens becomes thousands, and so on. The Mental Math on p. 28, and Lesson 5 highlight this connection between the place value system and certain calculations.

Planning for Instruction

Problem Solving

- Assign a Problem of the Week each week from the selection below (see sample answers on p. 69) or from your own collection:
  1. How long would it take you to count to 10 000? How could you find out?
  2. About how many pages of your local telephone book would you need to make a list of 10 000 names?
  3. Write a number that fits these rules:
     ○ The number is between 8000 and 10 000.
     ○ The sum of all the digits is an even number.
     ○ The hundreds digit is an odd number.
- Create a poster to keep track of problem-solving strategies used during the chapter. Put a checkmark beside the strategies that students will find most useful in this chapter.

Connections to Literature

Add books to your classroom that are related to the math in this chapter. For example:

The Grapes of Math (Greg Tang; Scholastic, 2001)

Marvelous Math: A Book of Poems (Lee Bennett Hopkins; Simon and Schuster, 1997)

Sea Squares (Joy N. Hulme; Hyperion, 1993)

Henry and the Boy Who Thought Numbers Were Fleas (Marjorie Kaplan; Macmillan, 1991)

The Great Pet Sale (Mick Inkpen; Orchard, 1999)

Under the Sun and Over the Moon (Kevin Crossley-Holland; Putnam, 1989)

Connections to Other Math Strands

Measurement: Students can find distances in kilometres
‣ to places they'd like to visit
- to places where relatives live
- between places they've been to
- between the provincial capital cities

Data Management: Students can be encouraged to organize any research findings into lists or tables so that the numbers are ordered from least to greatest. Students can also display their findings on a graph and explain how the 4-digit numbers compare to each other.

Connections to Other Curricula

Social Studies: Students can use reference books to look for 4-digit numbers such as population data, distances between places, lengths of rivers, depths of oceans, and heights of mountains. Have them compare and order sets of numbers associated with each topic.

Science: Many statistics about animals involve 4-digit numbers. Students can research things such as
- population of specific animals in a specific country
- number of different breeds worldwide of a specific animal
- amount of food eaten by a specific animal in a year

Physical Education: Students can look up world sports records that involve 4-digit numbers. Have students write and say the numbers in different ways.

Language Arts: Students can find rhymes and poems with numbers. Have them tell what would happen if each number was multiplied by 10, 100, or 1000. Students can rewrite the chants, songs, or poems so they still rhyme. For example, instead of "2, 4, 6, 8, who do we appreciate?" a student may write, "20, 40, 60, 80…we're so good, they call us great-y!"

Connections to Home and Community

- Have students start a collection of 4-digit numbers found at home or used in the community. For example, 2725 can be a house address, 1800 could be the seating capacity at the community theatre, 4537 could be the number of students enrolled at the community college, and so on.
- Send home the Family Newsletter (Master on p. 58)
- Have students complete the Math 4 Workbook pages for this chapter at home.
- Use the At Home suggestions found in most lessons.

Chapter 2 Planning Chart

Key Concepts

Numbers tell how many or how much.
Classifying numbers provides information about the characteristics and meaning of numbers.
There are different, but equivalent, representations for a number.
We use a number system based on patterns to make it easy to describe any possible number with just 10 digits. The value of any digit depends on its position in a numeral.
Benchmark numbers are useful for estimating and comparing numbers.

Chapter Goals

Understand and compare numbers to 10 000.
Represent 4-digit numbers in different ways.
Explore place value number patterns.
Communicate about ordering numbers.
Count and estimate money amounts.

Student Book Section	Lesson Goal	ON Expectation	Pacing 12 Days	Prerequisite Skills/Concepts
Getting Started: Modelling Numbers, pp. 28–29 (TR pp. 10–12)	Use concepts and skills developed prior to this chapter.	3m1, 3m2, 3m49, 3m50	1 day	• Model 3-digit numbers with base ten blocks. • Represent whole numbers using concrete materials. • Compare and order whole numbers using concrete materials. • Estimate, count, and record money amounts up to $10. • Read and write money amounts.
Lesson 1: Place Value, pp. 30–31 (TR pp. 13–16)	Model numbers up to 10 000.	4m7, 4m9, 4m12, 4m13	1 day	• Model 3-digit numbers with base ten blocks.
Lesson 2: Expanded Form, pp. 32–33 (TR pp. 17–20)	Write numbers up to 10 000 in expanded form.	4m9, 4m10, 4m12, 4m13, 4m16	1 day	• Read and print numbers from 0 to 1000. • Read and print number words to one hundred.
Lesson 3: Comparing and Ordering Numbers, pp. 34–35 (TR pp. 21–24)	Compare and order numbers up to 10 000.	4m2 , 4m9, 4m12, 4m13, 4m17	1 day	• Recognize and read whole numbers to 1000. • Compare and order whole numbers to 1000.
Lesson 4: Exploring 10 000, p. 36 (TR pp. 25–27)	Explore place value patterns up to 10 000.	4m2, 4m9, 4m12, 4m15	1 day	• Read and write 3-digit numbers from models and drawings.
Lesson 5: Multiplying by 10, 100, and 1000, pp. 38–39 (TR pp. 29–32)	Multiply by 10, 100, and 1000.	4m14, 4m15	1 day	• Model 3-digit numbers with base ten blocks. • Recognize that 10 ones blocks is equal to 1 tens block, and that 10 tens blocks is equal to 1 hundreds block.
Lesson 6: Rounding to the Nearest 10, 100, or 1000, pp. 42–43 (TR pp. 33–36)	Round numbers to the nearest 10, 100, or 1000.	4m15, 4m17	1 day	• Compare and order whole numbers to 10 000.
Lesson 7: Communicate About Ordering Numbers, pp. 44–45 (TR pp. 37–40)	Explain how to order a set of numbers in a complete, clear, and organized way.	4m2, 4m13, 4m15, 4m32	1 day	• Compare and order whole numbers to 10 000.
Lesson 8: Counting Money Collections, pp. 46–47 (TR pp. 41–44)	Estimate, count, and write money amounts up to $50.	4m47, 4m48	1 day	• Read and write money amounts using the dollar sign and decimal format (e.g., $0.89). • Estimate, count, and record the value in collections of coins and bills to $10. • Demonstrate the relationship between all coins and bills up to $100.
Mid-Chapter Review: p. 40 (TR p. 33) **Mental Math:** p. 37 (TR p. 28) **Math Game:** p. 41 (TR p. 35) **Skills Bank:** pp. 48–50 (TR pp. 49–50)	**Problem Bank:** p. 51 (TR pp. 51–52) **Chapter Review:** pp. 52–53 (TR pp. 53–54) **Chapter Task:** p. 54 (TR pp. 56–57)	3 days		

Materials	Masters/ Student Workbook	Extra Practice and Extension in the Student Book
base ten blocks (ones, tens, and hundreds) play money (bills and coins)	Place Value Mat: Hundreds, Tens, Ones, Masters Booklet, p. 37 (for Extra Support) Scaffolding Master, p. 65 (for Extra Support) Scaffolding Master, p. 66 (for Assessment) Initial Assessment Summary, Masters Booklet, p. 1	
base ten blocks (at least 10 each of hundreds, tens, and ones blocks for each group of students; as many thousand blocks as are available)	Mental Math Master p. 59 Place Value Mat: Hundreds, Tens, Ones, Masters Booklet, p. 37 Workbook p. 11	Mid-Chapter Review Question 1 Skills Bank Questions 1, 2 & 3 Problem Bank Questions 1 & 2
base ten blocks (ones, tens, hundreds, and thousands) (for Extra Challenge) several sets of number cards 0–9	Mental Math Master p. 59 Place Value Mat: Hundreds, Tens, Ones, Masters Booklet, p. 37 Workbook p. 12	Mid-Chapter Review Question 2 Skills Bank Questions 4, 5 & 6 Chapter Review Questions 1 & 2
base ten blocks (ones, tens, hundreds, and thousands) several sets of number cards 0–9	Mental Math Master p. 59 Place Value Mat: Hundreds, Tens, Ones, Masters Booklet, p. 37 (for Extra Support of Question 5) Scaffolding, p. 67 Workbook p. 13	Mid-Chapter Review Questions 4, 5, 6 & 7 Skills Bank Questions 7, 8, 9 & 10 Problem Bank Questions 3, 4 & 5 Chapter Review Questions 3, 4, 5, 6 & 7
base ten blocks (ones, tens, hundreds, and thousands) dice cards labelled *ones, tens, hundreds, thousands*	Mental Math Master p. 59 Workbook p. 14	Mid-Chapter Review Question 8 Skills Bank Questions 11 & 12 Chapter Review Question 8
base ten blocks (ones, tens, hundreds, and thousands) play money (bills) number cube labelled 1 to 6 number cube labeled *x 10, x 100, x 1000* (each label appears twice)	Mental Math Master p. 60 Place Value Mat: Hundreds, Tens, Ones, Masters Booklet, p. 37 Workbook p. 15	Mid-Chapter Review Question 9 Skills Bank Question 13 Problem Bank Question 6 Chapter Review Questions 9, 10, 11 & 12
(optional) number cards labelled 7000 and 8000	Mental Math Master p. 60 (for Extra Support) Number Lines, Masters Booklet, p. 32 (for Extra Support of Question 4) Scaffolding, p. 68 Workbook p. 16	Skills Bank Questions 14 & 15 Problem Bank Question 7 Chapter Review Questions 13, 14 & 15
(for Extra Challenge) several sets of number cards 0–9 (for Extra Support) base ten blocks (ones, tens, hundreds, and thousands)	Mental Math Master p. 60 (for Extra Support) Place Value Mat: Hundreds, Tens, Masters Booklet, p. 37 Workbook p. 17	Skills Bank Questions 16, 17 & 18 Problem Bank Questions 8 & 9
play money (bills and coins)	Mental Math Master p. 60 Workbook p. 18	Skills Bank Questions 19 & 20 Chapter Review Questions 16 & 17
	Chapter 2 Test Pages 1 & 2 Masters pp. 61–62 Chapter 2 Task Pages 1 & 2 Masters pp. 63–64 Workbook p. 19	

Planning for Assessment

The Chapter 2 Assessment Chart on the next page lists many opportunities for assessment using a variety of strategies: written questions, interview, short answer, investigation, observation, and product marking. To guide you, refer to the recording tools and samples provided in the Multi-Chapter Masters Booklet pages 1-16.

Managing Initial Assessment

- To see the specific assessment suggestions for Getting Started, refer to TR pages 10 to 12 in this booklet. This initial assessment opportunity includes the exploratory activity Modelling Numbers and four skills-based questions in Do You Remember?
- You may use other initial assessments involving informal interview or written questions; for example, your own diagnostic activity or Starting-the-Year Masters: Crossnumber Puzzle, p. 17, and Numeration Practice, p. 18, provided in the Multi-Chapter Masters Booklet.
- Use *Initial Assessment Summary* (Tool 1) to help you record your observations and concerns about the prior knowledge that an individual brings to Chapter 2. You may choose to record observations for all students, or for only those individuals who appear to have difficulty.

Managing Assessment for Feedback

- To see the specific assessment suggestions for Lessons 1 to 8, refer to the second column of the Chapter 2 Assessment Chart on the next page.
- You may use other informal feedback assessments involving ongoing observations and interviews to help you adapt your instruction to suit individual student needs.
- Use any of these tools to help you improve student achievement:
  What to Look For When Assessing Student Achievement (Tool 2),
    - *Coaching Students Towards Success* (Tool 3)
    - *Conducting In-Class Student Interviews, Student Interview Form* (with prompts) (Tool 4)
    - *Student Interview Form* (without prompts) (Tool 5)
- **Peer Assessment:** As students are working together, encourage them to listen to one another and assist if appropriate. Good opportunities for informal peer assessment occur in the Exploration Lesson 4, the Problem Solving strategy Lesson 5, and the Math Game: Getting to 10 000.
- **Self Assessment:** As students are working through the chapter, encourage them to practise at home. They can use the Skills Bank or the Workbook.
- **Journal Writing:** Good opportunities for journal writing occur in the Reflecting or the Consolidation section in any lesson.

Managing Assessment of Learning

- Refer to the last four columns of the Chapter 2 Assessment Chart on the next page. There you will find detailed support for all the Key Assessment Questions in Lessons 1 to 8, and all the questions in the Mid-Chapter Review and Chapter Review, as well as the Chapter Task. Which of these opportunities you choose to assess will depend on the quantity of evidence you need to gather for individual students.

  Note: When charts show levels of student achievement, they are always based on the appropriate parts of the four generic rubrics (scoring scales):
  Problem Solving Rubric (Tool 6),
  Understanding of Concepts Rubric (Tool 7),
  Application of Procedures Rubric (Tool 8),
  Communication Rubric (Tool 9).
- If you wish to assess other questions from the lessons or the Problem Bank or the Problems of the Week, use the appropriate rows from the four generic rubrics to create your own question-specific rubric.
- Use any of these tools to help you record and track student achievement:
    - *Using the Assessment of Learning Summary—Individual Student, Assessment of Learning Summary— Individual Student* (Tool 10)
    - *Using the Assessment of Learning Summary—Class by Strand, Assessment of Learning Summary—Class by Strand* (Tool 11)
- **Self Assessment:** After students have completed the chapter, encourage them to try Test Yourself on Workbook pp. 9-10. (Answers to these multiple choice questions can be found at www.mathk8.nelson.com)
- **Journal Writing:** A good opportunity for journal writing occurs in the Chapter Review. One prompt students might use is "This is how I would explain how to order 4-digit numbers...."

Managing Chapter Evaluation

- Look at the assessment data you've recorded throughout the chapter on Tools 10 and 11. Also include any end-of-chapter information from either the Chapter 2 Task Pages 1 & 2 pp. 63-64 or the Chapter 2 Test Pages 1 & 2 pp. 61-62. Determine the most consistent level for an individual.

Chapter 2 Assessment Chart

Student Book Lesson	Assessment for Feedback Chart	Assessment of Learning			
		Chart	Question/Category	ON Expectations	Strategy
Lesson 1: Guided Activity Place Value, pp. 30–31	TR p. 13	TR p. 16	4, Understanding of Concepts	4m12	written question
Lesson 2: Direct Instruction Expanded Form, pp. 32–33	TR p. 17	TR p. 20	5, Communication	4m10	written question
Lesson 3: Guided Activity Comparing and Ordering Numbers, pp. 34–35	TR p. 21x	TR p. 24	5, Understanding of Concepts, Application of Procedures	4m13	written question
Lesson 4: Exploration Exploring 10 000, pp. 30–31	TR p. 25	TR p. 28	entire exploration, Problem Solving	4m2, 4m12	investigation
Lesson 5: Guided Activity Multiplying by 10, 100, and 1000, pp. 38–39	TR p. 29	TR p. 32	5, Application of Procedures	4m14	written question
Mid-Chapter Review, p. 40			1, Understanding of Concepts	4m12	written question
			2, Communication	4m10	written question
			3, Communication	4m10	written question
			4, Communication	4m10	written question
			5, Communication	4m10	written question
			6, Understanding of Concepts	4m13	written question
			7, Understanding of Concepts	4m13	written question
			8, Application of Procedures	4m13	written question
			9, Application of Procedures	4m14	written question
Lesson 6: Direct Instruction Rounding to the Nearest 10, 100, or 1000, pp. 42–43	TR p. 37	TR p. 40	4, Communication, Understanding of Concepts	4m15	written question
Lesson 7: Direct Instruction Communicate About Ordering Numbers, pp. 44–45	TR p. 41	TR p. 44	3, Understanding of Concepts, Communication	4m13 4m32	written question
Lesson 8: Guided Activity Counting Money Collections, pp. 46–47	TR p. 45	TR p. 48	6, Understanding of Concepts	4m47, 4m48	written question
Chapter Review, pp. 52–53		TR p. 54	1, Communication, Understanding of Concepts	4m10, 4m12	written question
			2, Communication	4m10	written question
			3, Communication	4m10	written question
			4, Communication	4m10	written question
			5, Understanding of Concepts	4m13	written question
			6, Application of Procedures	4m13	written question
			7, Understanding of Concepts	4m13	written question
			8, Application of Procedures	4m14, 4m1	written question
			9, Application of Procedures	4m14, 4m30	written question
			10, Application of Procedures	4m14, 4m32	written question
			11, Application of Procedures	4m14	written question
			12, Application of Procedures	4m14	written question
			13, Understanding of Concepts	4m15	written question
			14, Understanding of Concepts	4m15	written question
			15, Understanding of Concepts	4m15	written question
			16, Understanding of Concepts	4m12, 4m15	written question
			17, Problem Solving	4m12, 4m30	written question
Chapter Task, p. 54	TR pp. 56-57		entire task, Problem Solving	4m2, 4m7, 4m10, 4m12, 4m15, 4m32	observation and product marking

Reading Strategies

Reading for Understanding	Reading Strategies
Getting Started **Reviewing the example:** Students will have a better understanding of how to complete the tasks to follow.	• Ask students to explain, in their own words, how the base ten blocks represent the number of animal and bird calls made by the man in India.
Lesson 1 **Building a mathematical vocabulary:** Students will have a better understanding of the meaning of place value.	• Have students explain the concept of regrouping in their own words. • Ask students to explain why it is important to use mathematical language.
Lesson 2 **Reading a chart:** Students will have a better understanding of how numbers can be written in expanded form.	• Ask students to explain the term *place value*. • Ask students what each column in the place value chart represents. • Have students explain the purpose of writing numbers in expanded form.
Lesson 3 **Representing a concept with symbols:** Students will be better able to compare and order numbers.	• Ask why symbols are sometimes used instead of words in mathematics. • Ask students to show < using their left thumb and first finger. Tell them that one way to remember the symbol for *less than* is that it can be made using the left hand (*less than* and *left* both start with the letter "l"). • Ask why it might be important to compare numbers.
Lesson 4 **Reading a title:** Students will have a better understanding of the activity that follows.	• Ask students to explain the purpose of a title. • Ask how the Mental Math title, "Adding Tens, Hundreds, and Thousands," helps them know what they are expected to do in the activity that follows.
Lesson 5 **Reading the lesson's goal:** Students will understand the purpose of the lesson.	• Ask students to explain why each lesson starts with a goal. • Ask them to identify the goal of this lesson and to predict what kinds of questions they will be asked to complete.
Mid-Chapter Review **Identifying key words and symbols:** Students will better understand how to respond to the question.	• Ask students to identify the words and symbols that tell them what they need to do in order to answer the questions (e.g., *model, expanded form, standard form,* > and <, etc.) • Ask how these words and symbols will help them respond appropriately to the questions.
Math Game **Reading and following procedures:** Students will understand how to play Getting to 10 000.	• Ask students to identify what materials they will need to play the game. • Ask how many people can play this game. • Ask them to explain the game in their own words.
Lesson 6 **Explaining rounding with a number line:** Students will have a better understanding of the purpose of rounding.	• Have students look at the number line and explain why the same number can be rounded in different ways. • Ask students to give examples of when they might use rounded numbers.
Lesson 7 **Building a mathematical vocabulary:** Students will understand the importance of clear, complete and organized language when communicating mathematical concepts.	• Modify strategies from Lesson 1 above.
Lesson 8 **Reading a table:** Students will be able to better understand the problem.	• Ask students to explain the purpose of the table. • Ask students what Paulette will have to do to solve the problem.
Skills Bank/Problem Bank/Chapter Review: **Finding key information:** Students will find the information they need to help solve the problems and answer the questions.	• Ask students what they can do to find the key information in the problems in the Problem Bank (e.g., read the problems, identify key words, estimate, read the table, etc.)
Chapter Task **Identifying key information**	• Modify strategies from Mid-Chapter Review above.

Chapter Opener

Using the Chapter Opener

Introduce this chapter by discussing the photograph on Student Book p. 27, which shows monarch butterflies gathering before migrating north to Canada. Tell the students that each spring about 200 million monarch butterflies migrate from Mexico to Canada and the Eastern United States. Some of the butterflies fly up to 4000 km to get to Canada. Then, in the fall, they return to Mexico.

Ask the class questions such as:

- How many butterflies do you think are shown on this page? (about 100)
- How many pages of butterflies like this do you think it would take to make 1000? (10)

Locate Mexico on a map and determine how far it is from where you live.

- Would a monarch butterfly that flies 4000 km to get to Mexico live closer or farther from Mexico than you?
- How do you know?

Have a brief class discussion about the five goals of the chapter. Ask students for examples of 3-digit and 4-digit numbers. Dictate some examples of 3- and 4-digit numbers and provide more in writing on the board. Ask students how many ones, tens, hundreds, and thousands are in each number.

Many of the students will have used base ten blocks before. Show the blocks that represent ones, tens, hundreds, and thousands. Review what each block represents. Write a 3-digit number on the board, read it aloud, and ask students how the number could be modelled using the base ten blocks. Ask students how they would model the distance some monarch butterflies fly one way (4 thousands blocks).

Tell students that just now they have seen a number written on the board, heard it said aloud, and modelled it with base ten blocks. Ask students to record in their journals their thoughts about the following goal: "The different ways that I can represent a 4-digit number are…"

At the end of the chapter, you can ask students to complete the same prompt and compare their responses and reflect on what they have learned.

At this time, it would be appropriate to

- send home the Family Newsletter
- ask students to look through the chapter and add math word cards to your classroom word wall. Here are some terms related to this chapter.

ones	standard form	bills
tens	expanded form	toonie
hundreds	base ten blocks	loonie
thousands	dollars	quarter
place value	cents	dime

Numeration

CHAPTER 2

Goals

You will be able to

- understand and compare numbers to 10 000
- represent 4-digit numbers in different ways
- explore place value number patterns
- communicate about ordering numbers
- count and estimate money amounts

Monarch butterflies gather before migrating north to Canada.

Family Newsletter Master, p. 58

Getting Started: Modelling Numbers

Grade 3 Skills/Concepts

- Model 3-digit numbers with base ten blocks.
- Represent whole numbers using concrete materials.
- Compare and order whole numbers using concrete materials.
- Estimate, count, and record money amounts up to $10.
- Read and write money amounts.

Use these pages as an opportunity for initial assessment to give you a sense of students' understanding of place value of 3-digit numbers, their skills in comparing and ordering numbers, and their experience with base ten blocks. Observe what students can do and what they're having difficulty with. Record your notes using the Initial Assessment Summary for each individual.

Preparation and Planning

Pacing	**30-40 min** Activity **10-20 min** Do You Remember?
Materials	• base ten blocks (ones, tens, and hundreds) • play money (bills and coins)
Resources	• (manipulatives substitute) Play Money 1, Masters Booklet, p. 27 • (manipulatives substitute) Base Ten Blocks, Masters Booklet, pp. 33-35 • Place Value Mat: Hundreds, Tens, Ones, Masters Booklet, p. 37 • (for Extra Support) Scaffolding, p. 65 • (for Extra Support) Scaffolding, p. 66 • (for Assessment) Initial Assessment Summary, Masters Booklet, p. 1
Vocabulary/ Symbols	base ten blocks, thousands, hundreds, tens, ones, place value, digit

CHAPTER 2

Getting Started

Modelling Numbers

A man in India has learned how to mimic the calls of 326 animals and birds.

Here is 1 way to represent 326 using base ten blocks.

11 blocks were used.

You will need
• base ten blocks
• play money

28

NEL

Using the Activity (Individual) ▶ 30-40 min

Show students base ten blocks (i.e., ones, tens, and hundreds) and review what each block represents. Have a student model 326 with base ten blocks. Then ask students to look at the drawing of the base ten blocks and the written number 326 on p. 28. Have students compare their model of base ten blocks to the drawing. Ask students how many blocks in total were used to model 326.

Part A Observe individual students to see if they can explain that 326 is greater than 300 because the model for 326 uses more blocks than just the 3 hundreds blocks. It is less than 400 because the rest of the blocks (the blocks other than the 3 hundreds blocks) do not make up another hundred. Students who cannot explain this should use base ten blocks to model 326 for themselves.

Part B and C Observe individual students to see if they can correctly model 326 with the specified parameters. Students who can answer these questions easily understand the trading relationship of the base ten blocks. If Extra Support is required, provide copies of **Place Value Mat: Hundreds, Tens, Ones, Masters Booklet, p. 37** and **Scaffolding Master p. 65**. Students can use the place value chart to model and trade blocks as necessary.

Part D-F There are two requirements for each of these parts: one is that students use exactly 11 blocks and the other is that they follow specific directions to create certain numbers. You may wish to have students work in pairs to ensure that they meet both requirements. For example, for Part D, one student can focus on the fact that the number created is the greatest number, and the other student can make sure that they use exactly 11 blocks. Observe each pair of students to see if they meet both requirements.

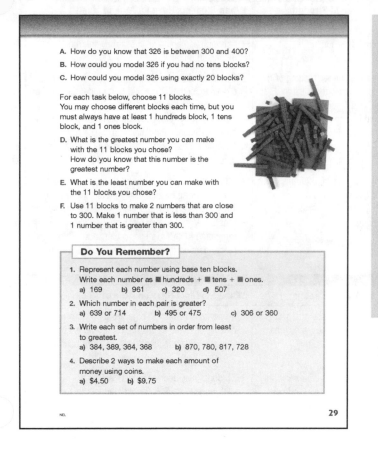

A. How do you know that 326 is between 300 and 400?

B. How could you model 326 if you had no tens blocks?

C. How could you model 326 using exactly 20 blocks?

For each task below, choose 11 blocks.
You may choose different blocks each time, but you must always have at least 1 hundreds block, 1 tens block, and 1 ones block.

D. What is the greatest number you can make with the 11 blocks you chose?
How do you know that this number is the greatest number?

E. What is the least number you can make with the 11 blocks you chose?

F. Use 11 blocks to make 2 numbers that are close to 300. Make 1 number that is less than 300 and 1 number that is greater than 300.

Do You Remember?

1. Represent each number using base ten blocks. Write each number as ■ hundreds + ■ tens + ■ ones.
   a) 169   b) 961   c) 320   d) 507

2. Which number in each pair is greater?
   a) 639 or 714   b) 495 or 475   c) 306 or 360

3. Write each set of numbers in order from least to greatest.
   a) 384, 389, 364, 368   b) 870, 780, 817, 728

4. Describe 2 ways to make each amount of money using coins.
   a) $4.50   b) $9.75

NEL   29

Using Do You Remember? (Individual)
▶ 10-20 min

Observe individual students to see if they can correctly answer the questions. If Extra Support is required, guide those students and provide base ten blocks and a copy of the **Place Value Mat: Hundreds, Tens, Ones, Masters Booklet, p. 37** and **Scaffolding p. 66.**

2. and 3. Students can model the numbers on a place value chart to help them make direct comparisons to determine which numbers are greater.

4. Students' answers will inform you who recalls the skills learned in Grade 3 of counting and recording collections of coins up to $10.00. Some students may need to physically manipulate play money in order to determine the coins needed to make each of these amounts.

1. a) 1 hundreds block, 6 tens blocks, 9 ones blocks
      1 hundred + 6 tens + 9 ones
   b) 9 hundreds blocks, 6 tens blocks, 1 ones block
      9 hundreds + 6 tens + 1 one
   c) 3 hundreds blocks, 2 tens blocks
      3 hundreds + 2 tens + 0 ones
   d) 5 hundreds blocks, 7 ones blocks
      5 hundreds + 0 tens + 7 ones

2. a) 714
   b) 495
   c) 360

3. a) 364, 368, 384, 389
   b) 728, 780, 817, 870

4. a) For example, 4 loonies and 2 quarters, or 2 toonies and 5 dimes
   b) For example, 9 loonies and 3 quarters, or 4 toonies, 1 loonie, 7 dimes, and 5 pennies

Answers

A. For example, 300 is the same as 3 hundreds blocks. There are more blocks than 3 hundreds though, so 326 has to be greater than 300. There are not enough tens and ones blocks to regroup for another hundred block to make 400. So, 326 must be between 300 and 400.

B. For example, 3 hundreds blocks and 26 ones blocks

C. 2 hundreds blocks, 12 tens blocks, and 6 ones blocks

D. For example, I have to have at least 1 hundreds block, 1 tens block, and 1 ones block. That makes 3 blocks. I can choose 8 more blocks, so I choose 8 of the largest block, the hundreds block. The number my 11 blocks make is 911.

E. For example, I have to have at least 1 hundreds block, 1 tens block, and 1 ones block. That makes 3 blocks. I can choose 8 more blocks, so I choose 8 of the smallest block, the ones block. The number my 11 blocks make is 119.

F. For example, 281 (2 hundreds blocks, 8 tens blocks, 1 ones block) and 317 (3 hundreds blocks, 1 tens block, 7 ones blocks).

Numbers	When Students Have an Area of Strength	When Students Have an Area of Need
• Part A (Understanding of Concepts)	• Students will be able to determine which two multiples of 100 a given 3-digit number is between.	• Students may not be able to see that 326 is between 300 and 400 unless they see the physical models of all numbers.
• Parts B and C (Application of Procedures)	• Students can demonstrate an understanding of the following regrouping concepts, without using blocks: 1 ten = 10 ones, and 1 hundred = 10 tens. Students can use this understanding to describe different representations of 3-digit numbers.	• Students who have difficulty using exactly 20 blocks to model 326 should first model the number with 3 hundreds blocks, 2 tens blocks, and 6 ones blocks. Review the following regrouping concepts: 1 ten = 10 ones, and 1 hundred = 10 tens. Encourage students to regroup the blocks in their model until they have exactly 20 blocks.
• Parts D-F (Application of Procedures)	• Students understand the regrouping relationships among hundreds, tens, and ones, and are able to model numbers with base ten blocks according to certain criteria in problems.	• Students may need to model each part of these questions step by step using a place value chart. They should start by placing a hundreds block, a tens block, and a ones block on their chart. For the remaining 8 blocks, students can choose blocks, place them on their charts, and determine if they meet the criteria of the problem.

Do You Remember?	When Students Have an Area of Strength	When Students Have an Area of Need
• Question 1 (Application of Procedures)	• Students will be able to relate numbers to a model and to the number of hundreds, tens, and ones in that number.	• Students may need to organize their thinking by placing base ten blocks on a place value chart to see a physical model of the number of hundreds, tens, and ones in a number.
• Question 2, 3 (Application of Procedures)	• Students will be able to compare 3-digit numbers based on the number of hundreds, tens and ones in the number.	• Students may need to model each of the numbers with base ten blocks. Direct students to compare the numbers by looking at the hundreds place first, then the tens place, then the ones place, as they look for a greater digit in the highest place value.
• Question 4 (Application of Procedures)	• Students will be able to draw or describe sets of coins of money amounts less than $10.	• Students may need to review the names of the coins and their values. Some students may have to physically manipulate play coins to count money amounts and describe sets of coins.

Place Value Mat: Hundreds, Tens, Ones, Masters Booklet, p. 37

Extra Support: Scaffolding Master, p. 65

Extra Support: Scaffolding Master, p. 66

 **Goal** Model numbers up to 10 000.

Prerequisite Skills/Concepts

- Model 3-digit numbers with base ten blocks.

Expectations

4m7 solve problems involving whole numbers (and decimals) and describe and explain the variety of strategies used

4m9 recognize and read numbers (from 0.01) to 10 000

4m12 represent the place value of whole numbers (and decimals from 0.01) to 10 000 using concrete materials, drawings, and symbols

4m13 compare and order whole numbers (and decimals from 0.01) to 10 000 using concrete materials, drawings, and symbols

Assessment for Feedback	What You Will See Students Doing...	
Students will	**When Students Understand**	**If Students Misunderstand**
• use base ten blocks to model 4-digit numbers	• Students will model 4-digit numbers correctly, using the thousands block to represent the digit in the thousands place, the hundreds blocks to represent the digit in the hundreds place, the tens blocks to represent the number in the tens place, and the ones blocks to represent the digit in the ones place.	• Students may make mistakes in modelling 4-digit numbers that have a 0. For example, for 1504, they may use 1 thousands block, 5 hundreds blocks and 4 tens blocks. Use a place value chart with headings to help students relate the digits to the correct blocks. Have students place the appropriate blocks on the chart.

Preparation and Planning

Pacing	**5–10 min** Introduction **10–20 min** Teaching and Learning **25–30 min** Consolidation
Materials	• base ten blocks (at least 10 each of hundreds, tens, and ones blocks for each group of students; as many thousand blocks as are available)
Masters	• Place Value Mat: Thousands, Hundreds, Tens, Ones, Masters Booklet, p. 36 • Mental Math, p. 59 • (manipulatives substitute) Base Ten Blocks, Masters Booklet, pp. 33–35
Workbook	p. 11
Vocabulary/ Symbols	base ten blocks, thousands, hundreds, tens, ones, place value, digit
Key Assessment of Learning Question	Question 4, Understanding of Concepts

Meeting Individual Needs

Extra Challenge

- Encourage students to write their own word problems similar to **Question 7**.
- Challenge students with **Question 7** by changing 100 more hamburgers sold each week to 101 or 110.

Extra Support

- Some students may need additional practice with 2- or 3-digit numbers before working with thousands. Have them practise modelling 2- and 3-digit numbers with base ten blocks.
- Additional review may be needed with the concept of regrouping (i.e., 10 ones is the same as 1 ten, and 10 tens is the same as 1 hundred). Play regrouping games such as "Race to 100." Students take turns rolling a die or pair of dice. They take as many ones blocks as the number on the dice. Whenever they have 10 ones blocks, they regroup them as a tens block. The student who first has 10 tens, which can be regrouped as a hundreds block, is the winner.

1. Introduction (Whole Class/ Small Groups) ▶ 5–10 min

Use base ten blocks to review modelling 3-digit numbers and regrouping. Each group of students should have at least 10 ones blocks, 10 tens blocks, and 10 hundreds blocks. You may need a quick review of what each block represents and how many of each type of block is equal to another type of block.

Reinforce the concept of *place value*: that the *place* a digit holds in a number determines its *value*. The 3 in 356 has a different value than the 3 in 238. When a number has a digit of 0, that digit still holds a place and tells us that there are 0 of whatever the place value is.

Sample Discourse

"Model the number 285 with the blocks. Add a tens block. What is this new number?"
• *295*

"What happens when you add another tens block?"
• *You have 10 tens so you have to regroup them as a hundreds block.*

"How would we write this new number?"
• *305*

Have students work in small groups to model 3-digit numbers and regroup blocks. Include examples that have them regroup 10 ones as 1 ten, and 10 tens as 1 hundred. Have students write the standard form of the 3-digit number of each of their models. Tell students they are going to model 4-digit numbers.

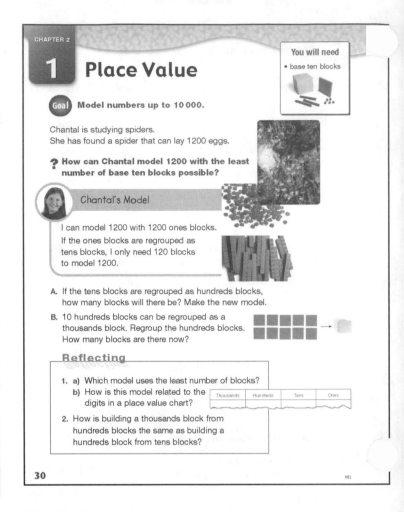

2. Teaching and Learning (Whole Class) ▶ 10–20 min

Have available a large number of ones and tens blocks, 12 hundreds blocks, and 1 thousands block.

Draw attention to the picture of the spider and its eggs. Allow a brief discussion of students' experiences with spiders. Point out that spiders can lay 1200 eggs and read the central question. Demonstrate Chantal's modelling of 1200 ones and her regrouping of 10 ones for 1 tens block. Ensure that students understand that Chantal is working her way to modelling 1200 with fewer blocks.

Answer the central question by answering prompts A and B. Demonstrate regrouping 10 tens blocks as 1 hundreds block, and when students tell you that 12 hundreds blocks are needed, model 1200 using 12 hundreds blocks. Then, introduce the thousands block. Show students how making 1 thousands block from 10 hundreds blocks is like making a 1 hundreds block from 10 tens blocks, or 1 tens block from 10 ones blocks. Model 1200 using 1 thousands block and 2 hundreds blocks.

Reflecting

Use these questions to ensure that students see that regrouping hundreds blocks as 1 thousands block is a natural extension of the regrouping they have done before. Discuss the questions, encouraging various responses.

1. a) • *The last model uses the least number. It only has 3 blocks. In the place value chart there would be a 1 in the thousands place—that's like 1 thousands block—and a 2 in the hundreds place—that's like 2 hundreds block.*

   b) • *The model with 1 thousands block and 2 hundreds blocks uses the least number. 1 thousands block is shown by the digit 1 in the thousands place in the place value chart, and 2 hundreds blocks are shown by the digit 2 in the hundreds place.*

2. • *It takes 10 of the smaller blocks to make 1 of the bigger blocks.*

   • *You can stack up 10 hundreds blocks and they are the same size as 1 thousands block, just like you can line up 10 tens blocks and they are the same size as 1 hundreds block.*

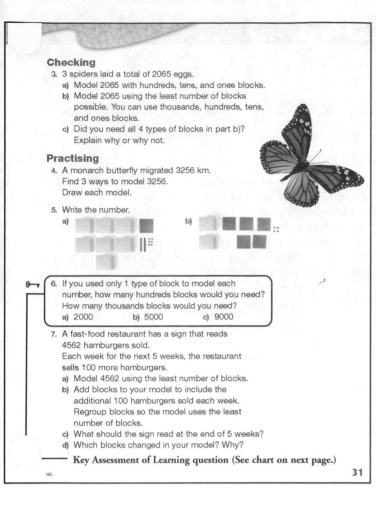

Checking

3. 3 spiders laid a total of 2065 eggs.
   a) Model 2065 with hundreds, tens, and ones blocks.
   b) Model 2065 using the least number of blocks possible. You can use thousands, hundreds, tens, and ones blocks.
   c) Did you need all 4 types of blocks in part b)? Explain why or why not.

Practising

4. A monarch butterfly migrated 3256 km. Find 3 ways to model 3256. Draw each model.

5. Write the number.
   a)
   b)

6. If you used only 1 type of block to model each number, how many hundreds blocks would you need? How many thousands blocks would you need?
   a) 2000   b) 5000   c) 9000

7. A fast-food restaurant has a sign that reads 4562 hamburgers sold.
   Each week for the next 5 weeks, the restaurant sells 100 more hamburgers.
   a) Model 4562 using the least number of blocks.
   b) Add blocks to your model to include the additional 100 hamburgers sold each week. Regroup blocks so the model uses the least number of blocks.
   c) What should the sign read at the end of 5 weeks?
   d) Which blocks changed in your model? Why?

   — Key Assessment of Learning question (See chart on next page.)

NEL   31

3. Consolidation ▶ 20-30 min

Checking (Small Groups)

For intervention strategies, refer to Meeting Individual Needs and the Assessment for Feedback chart.

The number 2065 can be modelled in a variety of ways using hundreds, tens, and ones blocks. Encourage students to try a variety of regroupings to find the least number of blocks required to model 2065.

Practising (Individual)

Encourage students to share base ten blocks and use them as needed before individually drawing the models or writing the numbers.

Related Questions to Ask

Ask	Possible Response
About **Question 6:** • Do you see a pattern between each number and the number of thousands and hundreds blocks needed?	• *The digit in the thousands place tells the number of thousands blocks. The first two digits (thousands and hundreds) tells the number of hundreds blocks.*

Closing (Whole Class)

Have students summarize their learning by asking, "Model 1550 with the least number of blocks. Tell how you know that you have used the least number."

• *I used 1 thousands block, 5 hundreds blocks, and 5 tens blocks. This is the fewest blocks possible because you need 10 of any one type of block to regroup to a larger block and the most I have of any one block is 5.*

Answers

A. 12

B. 3

1. a) B

  b) For example, the digit in each place tells you how many of each type of block to use.

2. For example, they are both made with 10 blocks. The thousands block is made from 10 hundreds blocks, and the hundreds block is made from 10 tens blocks.

3. a) 20 hundreds blocks, 6 tens blocks, 5 ones blocks

  b) 2 thousands blocks, 6 tens blocks, 5 ones blocks

  c) For example, No, I did not need a hundreds block because there was a 0 in the hundreds place.

4. For example, 3 thousands blocks, 25 tens blocks, 6 ones blocks; or 3 thousands blocks, 2 hundreds blocks, 5 tens blocks, 6 ones blocks; or 32 hundreds blocks, 5 tens blocks, 6 ones blocks

5. a) 7126

  b) 2504

6. a) 20 hundreds, 2 thousands

  b) 50 hundreds, 5 thousands

  c) 90 hundreds, 9 thousands

7. a) 4 thousands blocks, 5 hundreds blocks, 6 tens blocks, 2 ones blocks

  b) 4 thousands blocks, 6 hundreds blocks, 6 tens blocks, 2 ones blocks (starting week); 4 thousands blocks, 7 hundreds blocks, 6 tens blocks, 2 ones blocks (week 2); 4 thousands blocks, 8 hundreds blocks, 6 tens blocks, 2 ones blocks (week 3); 4 thousands blocks, 9 hundreds blocks, 6 tens blocks, 2 ones blocks (week 4); 4 thousands blocks, 10 hundreds blocks, 6 tens blocks, 2 ones blocks; or 5 thousands blocks, 6 tens blocks, 2 ones blocks (week 5)

  c) 5062

  d) For example, I added 5 hundreds blocks, but then I was able to regroup 10 hundreds for 1 thousands block, so both the thousands and hundreds blocks changed.

Assessment Strategy: written question
Understanding of Concepts

Question 4
• A monarch butterfly migrated 3256 km. Find 3 ways to model 3256. Draw each model. (Score correct responses out of 3.)

Extra Practice and Extension

• You might assign any of the questions related to this lesson, which are cross-referenced in the chart below.

Mid-Chapter Review	Student Book p. 40, Question 1
Skills Bank	Student Book p. 48, Questions 1, 2, & 3
Problem Bank	Student Book p. 51, Questions 1 & 2
Workbook	p. 11, all questions
Nelson Web Site	Visit www.mathk8.nelson.com and follow the links to *Nelson Mathematics 4*, Chapter 2.

Math Background

The place value concepts in this lesson extend from the concepts learned in earlier grades about 2- and 3-digit numbers. As students represent and model 4-digit numbers, they should develop an understanding of place value relationships and how the value of a digit in one place value is 10 times the value the same digit would have if it were in the place to the right. It is important for students to see this relationship in a concrete way, using blocks.

Special attention should be given to reading, writing, and modelling numbers with zero, emphasizing the importance of zeros as place holders, particularly when the zero is in the middle of the number. Using the place value chart will help students see why the zeroes are placed where they are.

Students should be able to read, write, and model given numbers, and also be able to recognize and work with 4-digit numbers in problem situations.

It is advisable to avoid the word "and" when reading a whole number (e.g., read 3082 as "three thousand eighty two" rather than "three thousand and eighty two"). Reserve "and" to indicate that a fractional (or decimal) amount follows the number.

At Home

• Students could read and write numbers between 1000 and 10 000 that they find in newspapers or magazines.
• Students might relate numbers to familiar situations such as distances in kilometres between places they have been or heard about, the number of days between important events in their lives, or the number of steps taken to walk to places in their neighbourhood.

Place Value Mat: Thousands, Hundreds, Tens, Ones, Masters Booklet, p. 36

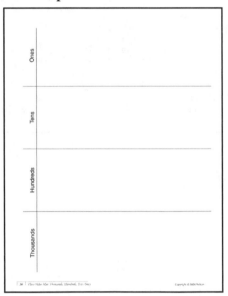

2 Expanded Form

Goal Write numbers up to 10 000 in expanded form.

Prerequisite Skills/Concepts

- Read and print numbers from 0 to 1000.
- Read and print number words to one hundred.

Expectations

4m9	recognize and read numbers (from 0.01) to 10 000
4m10	read and write whole numbers to 10 000 in standard, expanded, and written forms
4m12	represent the place value of whole numbers (and decimals from 0.01) to 10 000 using concrete materials, drawings, and symbols
4m13	compare and order whole numbers (and decimals from 0.01) to 10 000 using concrete materials, drawings, and symbols
4m16	identify the use of numbers in various careers

Assessment for Feedback	What You Will See Students Doing...	
Students will	**When Students Understand**	**If Students Misunderstand**
• read and print numbers from 0 to 10 000	• Students will read and print numbers from 0 to 10 000 correctly.	• Some students may have seen numbers written with a comma (e.g., 5,437). Tell them that 4-digit numbers do not need a comma.
• read and print number words to one thousand	• Students will read and print number words to one thousand correctly. When numbers with more than 3 digits are said aloud, there is no "and" in the number; 1547 is said as "one thousand, five hundred forty-seven," not "one thousand and five hundred and forty-seven."	• Some students may need reinforcement relating the different number forms: reading, writing, and saying numbers to reading, writing, and saying number words. Tell students that a number in one form is the same number even when it is written or said in another form.

Preparation and Planning

Pacing	**5–10 min** Introduction **15–20 min** Teaching and Learning **20–30 min** Consolidation
Materials	• base ten blocks (ones, tens, hundreds, and thousands) • (for Extra Challenge) several sets of number cards 0–9
Masters	• Mental Math, p. 59 • Place Value Mat: Thousands Hundreds, Tens, Ones, Masters Booklet, p. 36 • (manipulatives substitute) Base Ten Blocks, Masters Booklet, pp. 33-35
Workbook	p. 12
Vocabulary/ Symbols	standard form, expanded form
Key Assessment of Learning Question	Question 5, Communication

Meeting Individual Needs

Extra Challenge

- Students can challenge themselves by flipping over 4 cards from a set of number cards. They can make a 4-digit number from the cards and represent that number using the different forms: standard, expanded using numbers, expanded using words, saying it aloud.
- Another challenge is to have students use the same 4 cards and write as many different 4-digit numbers in standard and expanded form as they can.

Extra Support

- Use place value charts to reinforce the relationship between models of 3- and 4-digit numbers, their written expanded and standard forms, and the numbers written as words. Place blocks on the chart and have students write the number in expanded and standard forms. Ask students to say the number aloud.

1. Introduction (Whole Class)
▶ 5–10 min

Write the following number "staircase" on the board or chart paper:

```
 |5
 |70
 |200
 |6000
```

Repeat several times with other 4-digit numbers to show how staircases can be made from 4-digit numbers.

Sample Discourse

"Add all the numbers. What do you notice about the answer?"

- *The answer is 6275. All of the numbers in the staircase except for the zeros are in the answer. They are also in order.*

"Does it matter if you add up or down?"

- *No, because the number of zeros tells you what place the digit is in.*

Have students make up their own staircases in their notebooks. Tell students they are going to learn to represent 4-digit numbers in different ways.

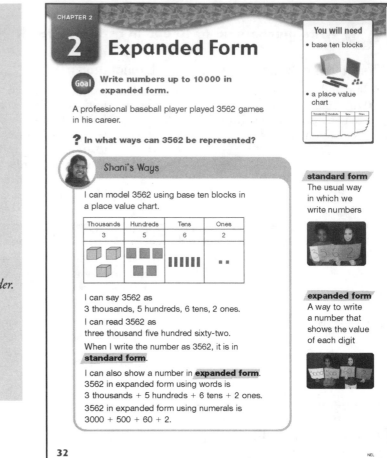

CHAPTER 2

2 Expanded Form

You will need
- base ten blocks
- a place value chart

Goal Write numbers up to 10 000 in expanded form.

A professional baseball player played 3562 games in his career.

? In what ways can 3562 be represented?

Shani's Ways

I can model 3562 using base ten blocks in a place value chart.

Thousands	Hundreds	Tens	Ones
3	5	6	2

I can say 3562 as
3 thousands, 5 hundreds, 6 tens, 2 ones.
I can read 3562 as
three thousand five hundred sixty-two.
When I write the number as 3562, it is in **standard form**.

I can also show a number in **expanded form**.
3562 in expanded form using words is
3 thousands + 5 hundreds + 6 tens + 2 ones.
3562 in expanded form using numerals is
3000 + 500 + 60 + 2.

standard form
The usual way in which we write numbers

expanded form
A way to write a number that shows the value of each digit

32   NEL

2. Teaching and Learning (Whole Class/Individual) ▶ 15–20 min

Ask a student to read the sentence at the top of p. 32. Talk about how many games 3562 represents. Ask students to think about how many years this player must have played baseball.

Draw attention to the central question. Have students individually model the number 3562 using place value charts and base ten blocks. Discuss the different ways that the number 3562 can be read or written. Write each of these ways on the board.

Draw attention to the vocabulary boxes on p. 32. Make sure students understand the difference between standard form and expanded form. Give several 4-digit examples to reinforce the terms. Be sure to use an example of a 4-digit number with one or more zeros as well. Talk about what to do with the places that have a zero in the place value chart when writing a number in standard and expanded form, and when saying a number aloud.

Reflecting

Use these questions to ensure that students understand that although the values of each place in a number does not affect the total, the order in which the digits are written in standard form does matter.

Discuss the questions, encouraging various responses.

Sample Discourse

1. • *500 + 3000 + 2 + 60 is confusing because the place values aren't in the same order as the number in standard form.*
   • *3000 + 500 + 60 + 2 makes more sense because I can squash the numbers together by taking out the zeros and then I get 3562.*

2. • *When I write 3062 in expanded form, I don't say "0 hundreds." I just skip the hundreds. But when I write 3562 in expanded form, I can't skip any numbers. I have to include them all.*
   • *When a number has a zero, I skip that place value when writing the number in expanded form. When a number has no zeroes, I have to include every place value.*

3. • *It takes less space when I write numbers in standard form.*
   • *Writing numbers in expanded form takes a really long time.*

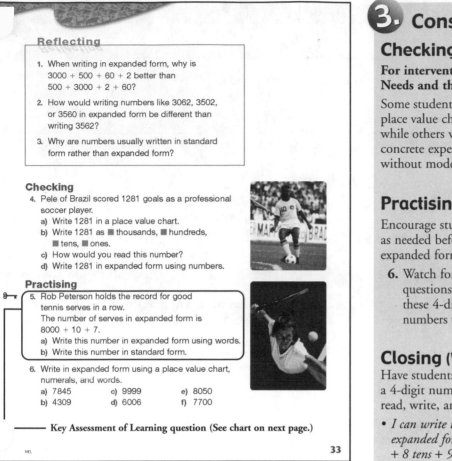

Reflecting

1. When writing in expanded form, why is 3000 + 500 + 60 + 2 better than 500 + 3000 + 2 + 60?

2. How would writing numbers like 3062, 3502, or 3560 in expanded form be different than writing 3562?

3. Why are numbers usually written in standard form rather than expanded form?

Checking

4. Pele of Brazil scored 1281 goals as a professional soccer player.
   a) Write 1281 in a place value chart.
   b) Write 1281 as ■ thousands, ■ hundreds, ■ tens, ■ ones.
   c) How would you read this number?
   d) Write 1281 in expanded form using numbers.

Practising

5. Rob Peterson holds the record for good tennis serves in a row.
   The number of serves in expanded form is 8000 + 10 + 7.
   a) Write this number in expanded form using words.
   b) Write this number in standard form.

6. Write in expanded form using a place value chart, numerals, and words.
   a) 7845   c) 9999   e) 8050
   b) 4309   d) 6006   f) 7700

—— Key Assessment of Learning question (See chart on next page.)

NEL   33

3. Consolidation ▶ 20-30 min

Checking (Small Groups)

For intervention strategies, refer to Meeting Individual Needs and the Assessment for Feedback chart.

Some students may still need to use base ten blocks and place value charts to determine the answers to this section, while others will have moved away from the need for the concrete experience and are ready to do these questions without modelling.

Practising (Individual)

Encourage students to share base ten blocks and use them as needed before individually writing the numbers in expanded form.

6. Watch for students who are incorrectly answering questions that involve zeros. Having students model these 4-digit numbers, and relating the 4-digit numbers to expanded and standard forms will help.

Closing (Whole Class)

Have students summarize their learning by giving them a 4-digit number and asking, "How many ways can you read, write, and say this number?"

• *I can write the number in standard form (4289), in expanded form using words (4 thousands + 2 hundreds + 8 tens + 9 ones), and in expanded form using numbers (4000 + 200 + 80 + 9). I can say 4 thousands, 2 hundreds, 8 tens, 9 ones. I can say four thousand two hundred eighty-nine.*

Answers

1. For example, the first way shows the digits in the same order as they would be in standard form.

2. For example, numbers with a 0 digit do not use all 4 place values when written in expanded form. For each 0 digit, that place value is not included in expanded form.

3. For example, numbers are usually written in standard form because it is more efficient.

4. a)

Thousands	Hundreds	Tens	Ones
1	2	8	1

   b) 1 thousands, 2 hundreds, 8 tens, 1 one

   c) one thousand two hundred eighty-one

   d) 1000 + 200 + 80 + 1

5. a) 8 thousands + 1 ten + 7 ones

   b) 8017

6. a)

Thousands	Hundreds	Tens	Ones
7	8	4	5

   7000 + 800 + 40 + 5
   7 thousands + 8 hundreds + 4 tens + 5 ones

   b)

Thousands	Hundreds	Tens	Ones
4	3	0	9

   4000 + 300 + 9
   4 thousands + 3 hundreds + 9 ones

   c)

Thousands	Hundreds	Tens	Ones
9	9	9	9

   9000 + 900 + 90 + 9
   9 thousands + 9 hundreds + 9 tens + 9 ones

   d)

Thousands	Hundreds	Tens	Ones
6	0	0	6

   6000 + 6
   6 thousands + 6 ones

   e)

Thousands	Hundreds	Tens	Ones
8	0	5	0

   8000 + 50
   8 thousands + 5 tens

   f)

Thousands	Hundreds	Tens	Ones
7	7	0	0

   7000 + 700
   7 thousands + 7 hundreds

Assessment Strategy: written question
Communication

Question 5
- Rob Peterson holds the record for good tennis serves in a row. The number of serves in expanded form is 8000 + 10 + 7.
   a) Write this number in expanded form using words.
   b) Write this number in standard form.
(Score correct responses out of 2.)

Extra Practice and Extension

- You might assign any of the questions related to this lesson, which are cross-referenced in the chart below.

Mid-Chapter Review	Student Book p. 40, Questions 2 & 3
Skills Bank	Student Book p. 48, Questions 4, 5, & 6
Chapter Review	Student Book p. 52, Questions 1 & 2
Workbook	p. 12, all questions
Nelson Web Site	Visit www.mathk8.nelson.com and follow the links to *Nelson Mathematics 4*, Chapter 2.

Math Background

Writing numbers in standard form and in expanded form using numerals is the most common way of representing large numbers at this grade level. However, students benefit from realizing that there are other ways of representing numbers and from observing how the different forms relate to one another. As students represent numbers in different ways, they develop a stronger understanding of regrouping that will later support their ability to add and subtract numbers.

At Home

- Students could ask family members when and how they use larger numbers at home, at work, or during leisure activities. The numbers and ideas could then be brought to class and shared.

Place Value Mat: Thousands, Hundreds, Tens, Ones, Masters Booklet, p. 36

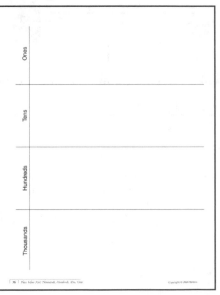

3 Comparing and Ordering Numbers

Goal **Compare and order numbers up to 10 000.**

Prerequisite Skills/Concepts

- Recognize and read whole numbers to 1000.
- Compare and order whole numbers to 1000.

Expectations

4m2	compare and order whole numbers (and decimals) using concrete materials and drawings
4m9	recognize and read numbers (from 0.01) to 10 000
4m12	represent the place value of whole numbers (and decimals from 0.01) to 10 000 using concrete materials, drawings, and symbols
4m13	compare and order whole numbers (and decimals from 0.01) to 10 000 using concrete materials, drawings, and symbols
4m17	identify and appreciate the use of numbers in the media

Assessment for Feedback	What You Will See Students Doing...	
Students will	**When Students Understand**	**If Students Misunderstand**
• represent the place value of numbers to 10 000	• Students will be able to model 4-digit numbers with base ten blocks.	• Students may model 4-digit numbers in any place value order. Tell them it is best to start modelling from left to right (e.g., from the thousands place to the ones place).
• compare and order whole numbers to 10 000	• Students will be able to explain why one 4-digit number is greater than another (e.g., they will compare the corresponding place values in the 2 numbers). Students will stop comparing digits after they find the greater number (e.g., for the numbers 875 and 234, students need only compare the hundreds digit).	• Some students may say a number is greater than another if it has a larger digit than the other number, regardless of the place value of the larger digit (e.g., they may say 1549 is larger than 1551). Give them base ten blocks to model and compare the numbers, starting with the thousands blocks. Ask students why they should start with the thousands block when comparing numbers. Watch for students who do not compare the digits from left to right.

Preparation and Planning

Pacing	**5–10 min** Introduction **10–15 min** Teaching and Learning **25–35 min** Consolidation
Materials	• base ten blocks (ones, tens, hundreds, and thousands) • several sets of number cards 0–9
Masters	• Mental Math, p. 59 • Place Value Mat: Thousands, Hundreds, Tens, Ones, Masters Booklet, p. 36 • (manipulatives substitute) Base Ten Blocks, Masters Booklet, pp. 33-35 • (for Extra Support of Question 5) Scaffolding, p. 67
Workbook	p. 13
Vocabulary/ Symbols	> and < symbols
Key Assessment of Learning Question	Question 5, Understanding of Concepts, Application of Procedures

Meeting Individual Needs

Extra Challenge

- Display the population data of several communities in your region with populations of less than 10 000. An alternative is to use the population data of schools in the region. Be sure to include a range of numbers. Challenge students to compare and order the populations from greatest to least. Discuss how to read the numbers correctly.
- Students can be challenged to research and find other populations to add to the list.
- Display a list of several communities and their distances from where students live. It might be interesting to use the same cities from the chart in **Question 5**. Challenge students to explain which is closest and which is farthest from where they live.

Extra Support

- Use place value charts and base ten blocks to reinforce the comparison and ordering of 4-digit numbers. Divide the chart in half horizontally and model two different numbers on the chart. Students can directly compare the number of blocks in each place.

Introduction (Whole Class)

▶ 5–10 min

Have two sets of four students stand at the front of the class. Each student holds up a number card so that each group represents a 4-digit number. The second group should kneel in front of the first group so that the two students representing each place value are visible, one behind the other. Model for the class how the two numbers can be compared by starting at the left to compare the thousands digit.

Discuss how to read each 4-digit number correctly. Repeat this activity so that all students have a turn. Tell students they are going to compare 4-digit numbers and put them in order.

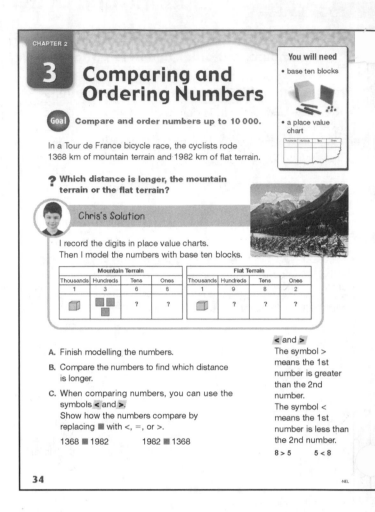

2. Teaching and Learning (Whole Class/Pairs) ▶ 10–15 min

Ask a student to read the sentence at the top of p. 34. Ask if anyone has heard of the Tour de France. Talk about the difference between mountain terrain and flat terrain.

Draw attention to the central question. Have children work in pairs and use place value charts and base ten blocks to model the numbers 1368 and 1982. Each student should model one of the numbers. Ask students how they can compare the two numbers. Elicit from the students the importance of comparing digits from left to right and that once they know a number has more hundreds, they don't need to compare the tens and ones digits.

Draw attention to the vocabulary box on p. 34. Provide some examples for students to reinforce the meaning of the symbols, then ask them to write a comparison sentence for the numbers 1368 and 1982 using < and >.

Reflecting

Use these questions to ensure that students understand why they need to start from the left when comparing numbers. To find a number between two other numbers, they must first find the largest place value by which the two other numbers differ. Tell students that they can check

their answer by comparing it to the numbers 1368 and 1982. Discuss the questions, encouraging various responses.

Sample Discourse

1. • *My answer is 1780. It has the same thousands digit as both 1368 and 1982. But I know 1780 is smaller than 1982 because the hundreds digit in 1982 is larger. And I know 1780 is greater than 1368 because the hundreds digit in 1780 is larger.*

   • *My answer is 1400. I know 1400 is between 1368 and 1982 because the digit in the thousands place is the same and the digit in the hundreds place in 1400 is greater than 3 and less than 9. The digits in the tens and ones place don't matter.*

2. • *The digit in the hundreds place are different. I know that the number with the larger digit in the hundreds place (1982) is larger than the number with the smaller digit in the hundreds place (1368). So 1982 is larger than 1368.*

   • *Once I find a place value with a different digit, I don't have to look at the rest of the number. I can already tell which number is larger.*

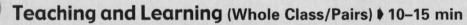

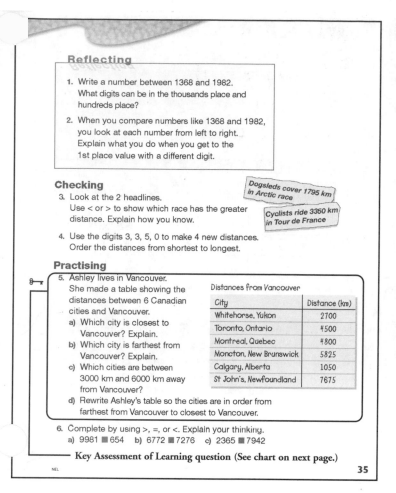

Reflecting

1. Write a number between 1368 and 1982. What digits can be in the thousands place and hundreds place?

2. When you compare numbers like 1368 and 1982, you look at each number from left to right. Explain what you do when you get to the 1st place value with a different digit.

Checking

3. Look at the 2 headlines. Use < or > to show which race has the greater distance. Explain how you know.

Dogsleds cover 1795 km in Arctic race

Cyclists ride 3350 km in Tour de France

4. Use the digits 3, 3, 5, 0 to make 4 new distances. Order the distances from shortest to longest.

Practising

5. Ashley lives in Vancouver. She made a table showing the distances between 6 Canadian cities and Vancouver.

   a) Which city is closest to Vancouver? Explain.

   b) Which city is farthest from Vancouver? Explain.

   c) Which cities are between 3000 km and 6000 km away from Vancouver?

   d) Rewrite Ashley's table so the cities are in order from farthest from Vancouver to closest to Vancouver.

Distances from Vancouver

City	Distance (km)
Whitehorse, Yukon	2700
Toronto, Ontario	4500
Montreal, Quebec	4800
Moncton, New Brunswick	5825
Calgary, Alberta	1050
St John's, Newfoundland	7675

6. Complete by using >, =, or <. Explain your thinking.
   a) 9981 ■ 654   b) 6772 ■ 7276   c) 2365 ■ 7942

— **Key Assessment of Learning question (See chart on next page.)**

NEL   **35**

Consolidation ▶ 25–35 min

Checking (Small Groups)

For intervention strategies, refer to Meeting Individual Needs and the Assessment for Feedback chart.

Some students may still need to use base ten blocks and place value charts to determine the answers to this section, while others will have moved away from the need for the concrete experience and are ready to do these questions without blocks. For **Question 4**, you may need to suggest a way for students to organize their numbers. Some students may want to use a place value chart and write the numbers in the places. Other students may use organized lists (e.g., all the 4-digit numbers that start with 5).

Practising (Individual)

Encourage students to share base ten blocks and use them as needed before individually comparing the numbers.

5. This question involves ordering and comparing distances. Students who are subtracting one distance from another do not understand the question. If students require Extra Support, provide them with copies of **Scaffolding Master p. 67.**

Closing (Whole Class)

Have students summarize their learning by asking, "Canada is 5514 km from east to west and 4634 km from north to south. Which distance is longer? How do you know?"

• *The distance from east to west is longer: 5514 > 4634*

Answers

A. 1 thousands block, 3 hundreds blocks, 6 tens blocks, 8 ones blocks; 1 thousands block, 9 hundreds blocks, 8 tens blocks, 2 ones blocks

B. For example, the thousands digits are 1 and 1, the hundreds digits are 3 and 9, the tens digits are 6 and 8, the ones digits are 8 and 2. Because 1982 has a larger hundreds digit, it is the larger number. The flat terrain is longer.

C. 1368 < 1982; 1982 > 1368

1. For example, 1780. The digit in the thousands place must be a 1. The digit in the hundreds place must be greater than 4 and less than 9.

2. For example, you compare the two numbers and determine which is greater.

3. 3350 > 1795 For example, there are more thousands in 3350 than 1795.

4. For example, any 4 of the following numbers placed in this order: 3035, 3053, 3305, 3350, 3503, 3530, 5033, 5303, 5330

5. a) Calgary. For example, its distance is the smallest number in the table. It has a 1 in the thousands place and all the other distances have a digit in the thousands place that is greater than 1.

b) St. John's. For example, it has the greatest digit in the thousands place.

c) Toronto, Montreal, and Moncton

d)

City	Distance (km)
St. John's	7675
Moncton	5825
Montreal	4800
Toronto	4500
Whitehorse	2700
Calgary	1050

6. a) 9981 > 654 For example, 9981 has a thousands digit and 654 does not.

b) 6772 < 7276 For example, 7276 has a greater thousands digits than 6772.

c) 2365 < 7942 For example, 7942 has a greater thousands digits than 2365.

Assessment Strategy: written question
Understanding of Concepts, Application of Procedures

Question 5

- Ashley lives in Vancouver. She made a table showing distances between 6 Canadian cities and Vancouver.
  a) Which city is closest to Vancouver? Explain.
  b) Which city is farthest from Vancouver? Explain.
  c) Which cities are between 3000 km and 6000 km away from Vancouver?
  d) Rewrite Ashley's table so the distances are in order from farthest from Vancouver to closest to Vancouver.

Student Name	correct response for a) and b) (Score 1 each for a total of 2)	provides complete explanation of thinking for a) and b) (Score 1 each for a total of 2)	c) correctly identifies cities (Score 1 each for a total of 2)	d) rewritten table is correct (Score 3)	d) rewritten table is partially correct (Score 1)	Total out of 9
Jorge	2	2	2		1	7
Isabel	1	1	2		1	5

Extra Practice and Extension

- You might assign any of the questions related to this lesson, which are cross-referenced in the chart below.

Mid-Chapter Review	Student Book p. 40, Questions 4, 5, 6, & 7
Skills Bank	Student Book p. 49, Questions 7, 8, 9, & 10
Problem Bank	Student Book p. 51, Questions 3, 4, & 5
Chapter Review	Student Book p. 52, Questions 3, 4, 5, 6, & 7
Workbook	p. 13, all questions
Nelson Web Site	Visit www.mathk8.nelson.com and follow the links to *Nelson Mathematics 4*, Chapter 2.

Math Background

It is important that students talk about the value of the digits they are comparing and not simply do a rote comparison of the digits, working from left to right. While this lesson does not deal directly with the concept of comparing numbers with different numbers of digits, you may wish to encourage students to compare such numbers. Some students will observe, for example, that a 3-digit number is always less than a 4-digit number.

Although this can be explained to students by telling them that the thousands digit of a 3-digit number is always 0, it is probably more easily understood if you say that all 3-digit numbers are less than 1 thousand and all 4-digit numbers are equal to or greater than 1000.

It is interesting to observe students as they compare numbers to see if they realize that

- it makes sense to always start at the left
- once they have established that a number has more thousands than another, it is not necessary to compare the hundreds, tens, or ones digits

At Home

- Students could gather real data from their community and compare the numbers. For example, which holds more people: the ice arena or the football stadium? Are there more people living in their community or in the community where their grandmother lives?

Place Value Mat: Thousands, Hundreds, Tens, Ones, Masters Booklet, p. 36

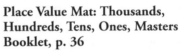

Extra Support: Scaffolding Master, p. 67

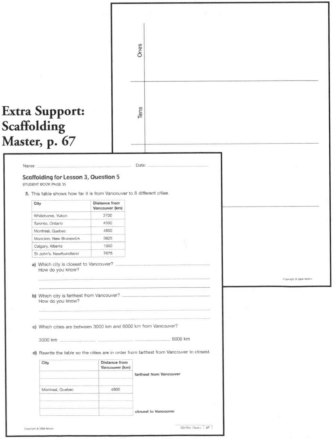

4 Exploring 10 000

 Goal Explore place value patterns to 10 000.

Prerequisite Skills/Concepts

• Read and write 3-digit numbers from models and drawings.

Expectations

4m2 compare and order whole numbers (and decimals) using concrete materials and drawings

4m9 recognize and read numbers (from 0.01) to 10 000

4m12 represent the place value of whole numbers (and decimals from 0.01) to 10 000 using concrete materials, drawings, and symbols

4m15 represent and explain number concepts and procedures

Assessment for Feedback	What You Will See Students Doing...	
Students will	**When Students Understand**	**If Students Misunderstand**
• Read and write 4-digit numbers from models and drawings	• Students will be able to correctly write a 4-digit number in standard form from models such as base ten blocks or counters on a place value chart, as well as from drawings representing those models.	• Students may make mistakes in writing 4-digit numbers from models or drawings that do not have any manipulatives in a given place value. For example, students may write the following model as 327 instead of 3027: Use a place value chart to directly relate the manipulatives to the places so that it is clear that a 0 needs to be used in the place value without manipulatives.

Preparation and Planning

Pacing	**5–10 min** Introduction **25–35 min** Teaching and Learning **10–15 min** Consolidation
Materials	• base ten blocks (ones, tens, hundreds, and thousands) • dice • cards labelled *ones, tens, hundreds, thousands*
Resources	• Mental Math, p. 59 • (manipulatives substitute) Base Ten Blocks, Masters Booklet, pp. 33-35
Workbook	p. 14
Key Assessment of Learning Question	Entire exploration, Problem Solving

Meeting Individual Needs

Extra Challenge

• The patterns on p. 36 involve changing only one type of block. Students can be challenged to create a pattern that leads to 10 000 as the fourth number, but to do so by changing two types of blocks (e.g., start with 9967 and increase both the tens and ones blocks by 1 for each number).

• Students can use a calculator to demonstrate the patterns on p. 36, and then to create their own patterns that lead to 10 000.

Extra Support

• Some students might have difficulty recognizing the patterns. Have them model and describe the following simpler patterns:

• Pattern 1 starts with 7 thousands blocks. The number of thousands blocks increases by 1 for each number.

• Pattern 2 starts with 9 thousands + 7 hundreds. The number of hundreds blocks increase by 1 for each number.

• Pattern 3 starts with 9 thousands + 9 hundreds + 7 tens. The number of tens blocks increase by 1 for each number.

Have students record the patterns as they model them.

Introduction (Whole Class)

▶ **5–10 min**

Discuss with students what a number pattern is and ask them to provide an example.

Sample Discourse

"What is a number pattern? Can anyone give an example?"
- *In a number pattern, the numbers change by the same amount, like 2, 4, 6, 8.*

"Can anyone suggest a number pattern with larger numbers?"
- *100, 200, 300, 400, 500*

"In the first pattern, the numbers changed by ones, and in the second pattern, the numbers changed by hundreds."

Roll a die four times and ask each student to individually create a 4-digit number from the numbers rolled. Have students model their number with base ten blocks.

Take four cards labelled *ones, tens, hundreds,* and *thousands.* Have a student choose one of the cards. Ask all students to create a number pattern by increasing their number's place value shown on the card four times. For example, if a student's number is 6432 and the place value card chosen is tens, that student's pattern is 6432, 6442, 6452, 6462.

Ask students to read their numbers. Have them describe their number pattern by telling which place value changed. Tell students they are going to look at patterns that lead to large numbers.

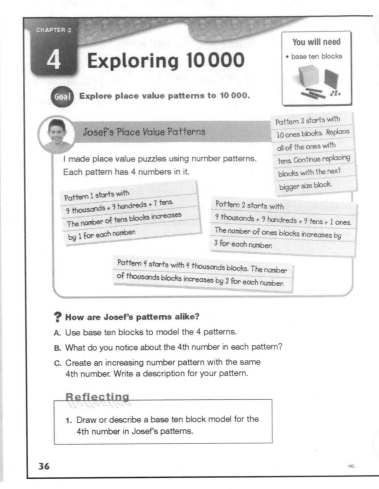

Teaching and Learning (Whole Class/Pairs) ▶ 25–35 min

Draw attention to the central question. Have students work in pairs to model each of Josef's patterns using base ten blocks. As they model the patterns, they can record each number on the board. Ask them to look for similarities between Josef's place value patterns and the ones they created in the Introduction activity.

Before assigning the Reflecting question, discuss the answers to B and C.

Sample Discourse

"What number did Josef start with in pattern 1?"
- *9970*

"What happened when Josef added 1 ten?"
- *It became 9980.*

"What are the next two numbers in this pattern?"
- *9990, 10 000*

Repeat this discourse with the other patterns.

Reflecting

Have students think about the different ways Josef's patterns reached 10 000 (e.g., some of the patterns involved increasing the ones; others increased the tens, hundreds, or thousands). Discuss the question, encouraging various models.

Sample Discourse

1. • *A ten thousands block could be made up of 10 thousands blocks.*
   • *A base ten model of 10 000 could have 1000 tens blocks.*

Answers

A. Pattern 1

9 thousands blocks, 9 hundreds blocks, 7 tens blocks;
9 thousands blocks, 9 hundreds blocks, 8 tens blocks;
9 thousands blocks, 9 hundreds blocks, 9 tens blocks;
9 thousands blocks, 9 hundreds blocks, 10 tens blocks
= 9 thousands blocks, 10 hundreds blocks
= 10 thousands blocks

Pattern 2

9 thousands blocks, 9 hundreds blocks, 9 tens blocks,
1 ones block; 9 thousands blocks, 9 hundreds blocks,
9 tens blocks, 4 ones blocks; 9 thousands blocks,
9 hundreds blocks, 9 tens blocks, 7 ones blocks;
9 thousands blocks, 9 hundreds blocks, 9 tens blocks,
10 ones blocks = 9 thousands blocks, 9 hundreds blocks,
10 tens blocks = 9 thousands blocks, 10 hundreds blocks
= 10 thousands blocks

Pattern 3

10 ones blocks; 10 tens blocks; 10 hundreds blocks;
10 thousands blocks

Pattern 4

4 thousands blocks; 6 thousands blocks; 8 thousands
blocks; 10 thousands blocks

B. The fourth number in each pattern is 10 000.

C. For example, 9100, 9400, 9700, 10 000. The pattern
starts with 9 thousands blocks and 1 hundreds blocks.
The number of hundreds blocks increases by 3 for
each number.

1. For example, it might look like 10 thousands blocks all
lined up like a giant tens block.

Math Background

An interesting model for 10 000 can be created with 10
thousands blocks. This emphasizes the parallel in the place
value system of 10 000 grouped by thousands with 10
grouped by ones. By placing a line of 10 ones blocks next
to the line of 10 thousands blocks, students will see that
each one has been expanded to a thousand.

3. Consolidation ▸ 10–15 min

For intervention strategies, refer to the Meeting
Individual Needs box or the Assessment for
Feedback chart.

Closing (Whole Class)

Have students summarize their learning by asking, "Create
a number pattern where the fourth number is 1000."

- *I can start with 997, and add 1 ones block each number.*
- *I can also start with 970 and add 1 tens block
each number.*

Extra Practice and Extension

- You might assign any of the questions related to this lesson,
which are cross-referenced in the chart below.

Mid-Chapter Review	Student Book p. 40, Question 8
Skills Bank	Student Book p. 49, Questions 11 & 12
Chapter Review	Student Book p. 53, Question 8
Workbook	p. 14, all questions
Nelson Web Site	Visit www.mathk8.nelson.com and follow the links to *Nelson Mathematics 4*, Chapter 2.

Problem Solving Rubric,
Masters Booklet p. 7

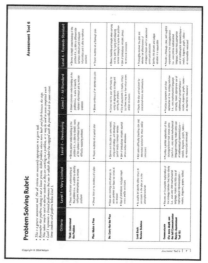

Assessment of Learning—What to Look for in Student Work...

Assessment Strategy: exploration

The focus is on Problem Solving.

Assessment Opportunity

In this exploration lesson the entire investigation is an opportunity for assessment. You will see students carrying out an inquiry and will be able to observe their ability to
use base ten blocks to model number patterns related to place value up to 10 000. You will also see them describe their observations about the results and create and
describe their own number pattern using the same criteria.

To gather evidence about a student's ability to problem solve, use informal observation and questioning. Use the Problem Solving Rubric (Tool 6) to help you focus on the
problem-solving process. You may wish to focus on the "Carry Out the Plan" and "Look Back" rows in the rubric.

Mental Math: Adding Tens, Hundreds, and Thousands

Using Mental Math

Materials: spinner (divided into five sections, labelled 1000 – 5000), dice, base ten blocks (thousands)

Roll the die and record the numbers vertically on the board as an addition problem.

For example: 2
             + 4

Have students do the sum in their heads. Record the sum. Then tell students that the numbers rolled on the die tell them how many thousands blocks to take. Have a student model the two addends using thousands blocks.

Record on the board next to the previous addition problem:

       2 thousands
     + 4 thousands

Ask students how knowing 2 + 4 helps them calculate the solution to this addition problem. Record on the board the problem in digits next to the other sums:

       2000
     + 4000
     ──────
       6000

Repeat with a number of dice throws.

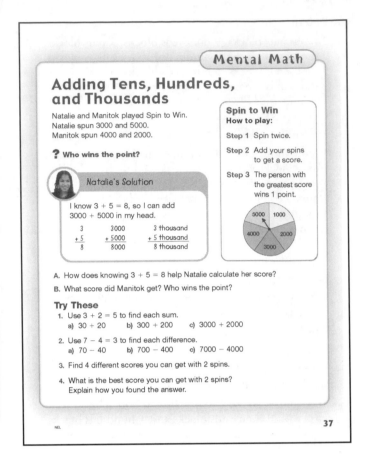

A. How does knowing 3 + 5 = 8 help Natalie calculate her score?

B. What score did Manitok get? Who wins the point?

Try These

1. Use 3 + 2 = 5 to find each sum.
   a) 30 + 20   b) 300 + 200   c) 3000 + 2000

2. Use 7 − 4 = 3 to find each difference.
   a) 70 − 40   b) 700 − 400   c) 7000 − 4000

3. Find 4 different scores you can get with 2 spins.

4. What is the best score you can get with 2 spins? Explain how you found the answer.

Answers

A. For example, Natalie knows that 3 + 5 = 8. When she looks at 3000 + 5000, she mentally removes the zeroes, thinks 3 + 5 = 8, then puts the same number of zeroes back. So 3 thousands + 5 thousands must = 8 thousands.

B. 6000; Natalie

1. a) 50
   b) 500
   c) 5000

2. a) 30
   b) 300
   c) 3000

3. For example, 2000 + 2000 = 4000; 3000 + 4000 = 7000; 4000 + 5000 = 9000; 3000 + 1000 = 4000

4. 10 000; for example, the most you can get on one spin is 5000. If you spin 5000 twice, you get 10 000.

5 Multiplying by 10, 100, and 1000

Goal **Multiply by 10, 100, and 1000.**

Prerequisite Skills/Concepts

- Model 3-digit numbers with base ten blocks.
- Recognize that 10 ones blocks is equal to 1 tens block, and that 10 tens blocks is equal to 1 hundreds block.

Expectations

4m14 multiply whole numbers by 10, 100, and 1000
4m15 represent and explain number concepts and procedures

Assessment for Feedback	What You Will See Students Doing...	
Students will	**When Students Understand**	**If Students Misunderstand**
• recognize that 10 ones blocks = 1 tens block, 10 tens blocks = 1 hundreds block, and 10 hundreds blocks = 1 thousands block	• Students will be able to recognize the relationships between the ones, tens, hundreds, and thousands blocks.	• Students who are not clear about the relationships between the blocks should spend time "making" one block using lower place value blocks (e.g., have students line up 10 tens blocks to see that they are physically the same size as 1 hundreds block).

Preparation and Planning

Pacing	**5–10 min** Introduction **10–15 min** Teaching and Learning **25–35 min** Consolidation
Materials	• base ten blocks (ones, tens, hundreds, and thousands) • play money (bills) • number cube labelled 1 to 6 • number cube labeled *x 10, x 100, x 1000* (each label appears twice)
Resources	• Mental Math, p. 60 • Place Value Mat: Thousands, Hundreds, Tens, Ones, Masters Booklet, p. 36 • (manipulatives substitute) Base Ten Blocks, Masters Booklet, pp. 33-35
Workbook	p. 15
Key Assessment of Learning Question	Question 5, Application of Procedures

Meeting Individual Needs

Extra Challenge

- Students can choose numbers of significance to them (e.g., their age, their birth date, the number of people in their family, the number of their classroom, etc.) Challenge students to tell how that number would change if they multiplied it by 10, 100, and 1000.
- Use two number cubes, one labelled 1 to 6 and the other labelled with two each of *x 10, x 100*, and *x 1000*. Students take turns rolling the two number cubes. Their score for each turn is the number on the cube labelled 1 to 6 multiplied by the power of 10 from the other cube. The first player to reach 10 000 wins.
- Students can use calculators to explore any patterns derived by pressing x 10, x 100, or x 1000.

Extra Support

- Reinforce the multiplication pattern by displaying a number of ones blocks (e.g., 5). Write *5 ones = 5* on the board. Then show 5 tens blocks. Write *5 tens = 50*. Show 5 hundreds. Write *5 hundreds = 500*. Talk with students about the pattern they see.
Repeat the activity starting with a different number of ones blocks.

1. Introduction (Whole Class) ▶ 5–10

Tell the students that a fabric store has ordered some buttons. The buttons are packaged on cards. There are 10 buttons on a card, and 10 cards in a box. You might show students a sample card with 10 buttons. Ask: "How many buttons are in a box?"

Write the following on the board and work through the problem with the students to determine how many buttons are in a box.

    10 buttons on a card
    10 cards in a box
         buttons in a box

Sample Discourse

"If there are 10 cards in a box, how can we find out how many buttons are in a box?"
• *You could add 10 ten times and get 100.*

"Is there a way we could find out using multiplication?"
• *You could say 10 x 10 and get 100.*

Tell students they are going to find and use patterns to help them multiply by 10, 100, and 1000.

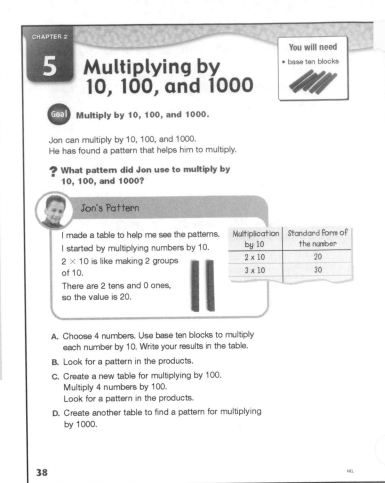

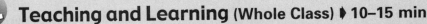

2. Teaching and Learning (Whole Class) ▶ 10–15 min

Write the headings *x 1*, *x 10*, *x 100*, and *x 1000* on the board. Show students two tens blocks and ask them to write a multiplication sentence to go with the blocks. Write 2 x 10 = 20 under the *x 10* heading. Show a variety of sets of base ten blocks and have students write multiplication sentences to go with the blocks.

Repeat until you have at least 4 number sentences under each heading. Ask students to identify any patterns they see.

Direct attention to the central question and ask students to explain how they would use what they have learned about Jon's pattern to answer the question.

Reflecting

Use these questions to ensure that students aren't relying on rote to place the correct number of zeroes behind a given number; rather, that they see how multiplying by 10, 100, and 1000 relates to the number of blocks, and that the type of block determines the number of zeros. Discuss the questions, encouraging various responses.

Sample Discourse

1. a) • *When I multiply a number by 10, it moves one place to the left. It moves from the ones place to the tens place.*

• *When I multiply a number by 10, it's as if I traded my ones blocks for tens blocks.*

b) • *Multiplying a number by 100 moves that number two places to the left, from the ones place to the hundreds place.*

• *When I multiply a number by 100, it's like trading a ones blocks for a hundreds blocks.*

c) • *When I multiply by 1000, the number I'm multiplying moves three places to the left, from the ones place to the thousands place.*

• *Multiplying a number by 1000 is like trading a ones blocks for a thousands blocks.*

2. • *There are no ones in 10, 100, or 1000 because there are zeros in the ones place. When you multiply by 10, 100, or 1000, you can only add more tens, hundreds, or thousands. You can't add any ones. So your answer will never have a number in the ones place. It will always end in zero.*

Reflecting

1. What pattern do you see when you multiply by each number?
   a) 10   b) 100   c) 1000

2. Why does it make sense that there will be 0 ones when you multiply a number by 10, 100, or 1000?

Checking

3. Use the patterns you found to multiply.
   a) 14 × 10   b) 61 × 100   c) 2 × 1000

4. What is the missing number?
   a) 2500 = ■ × 100   b) 2500 = ■ × 10

Practising

5. Multiply.
   a) 99 × 10   c) 1000 × 10   e) 15 × 100
   b) 5 × 1000   d) 10 × 1000   f) 100 × 100

6. For 10 years, Darren's parents have made him a photo album for his birthday. Each photo album has 144 photographs. How many photographs does Darren have in total?

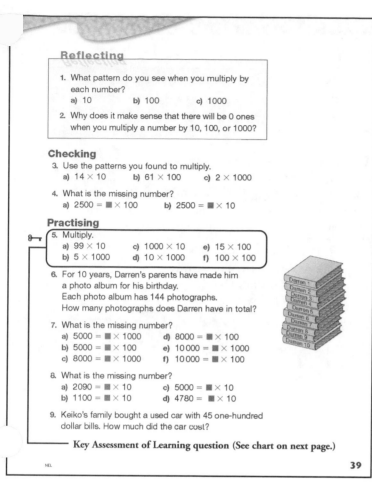

7. What is the missing number?
   a) 5000 = ■ × 1000   d) 8000 = ■ × 100
   b) 5000 = ■ × 100   e) 10 000 = ■ × 1000
   c) 8000 = ■ × 1000   f) 10 000 = ■ × 100

8. What is the missing number?
   a) 2090 = ■ × 10   c) 5000 = ■ × 10
   b) 1100 = ■ × 10   d) 4780 = ■ × 10

9. Keiko's family bought a used car with 45 one-hundred dollar bills. How much did the car cost?

— **Key Assessment of Learning question (See chart on next page.)**

---

3. Consolidation ▸ 25–35 min

Checking (Small Groups)

For intervention strategies, refer to the Meeting Individual Needs box or the Assessment for Feedback chart.

Students may use the base ten blocks to model these questions.

4. This question involves solving for a missing factor, which some students may have difficulty with. You may wish to rewrite the questions in the format of ___ × 100 = 2500.

Practising (Individual)

Encourage students to use base ten blocks as needed.

6. This problem has students using the pattern of multiplying by 10 to find the answer. Base ten blocks would not be a good model of the problem, as it involves 10 groups of 144, not 144 groups of 10.

Closing (Whole Class)

Have students summarize their learning by asking them to write a journal entry describing what it means to multiply a number by 10, by 100, and by 1000.

1. a) For example, when you multiply by 10, each digit moves one space to the left on a place value chart. The ones digit becomes the tens digit. There is nothing left in the ones place, so you put a zero there.
   b) For example, when you multiply by 100, each digit moves two spaces to the left on a place value chart. The tens digit becomes the thousands digit and the ones digit becomes the hundreds digit. There is nothing left in the ones and tens places, so you put zeroes in each of those places.
   c) For example, when you multiply by 1000, each digit moves three places to the left on a place value chart. This means there will be a zero in the ones, tens, and hundreds place.

2. For example, when you multiply by 10, or 100, or 1000, you are saying that a number is made up entirely of 10s, 100s, or 1000s. There are no ones, so there will always be a 0 in the ones place.

3. a) 140   b) 6100   c) 2000
4. a) 25   b) 250
5. a) 990   b) 5000   c) 10 000
   d) 10 000   e) 1500   f) 10 000
6. 144 x 10 = 1440; He has 1440 photos.
7. a) 5   b) 50   c) 8
   d) 80   e) 10   f) 100
8. a) 209   b) 110   c) 500   d) 478
9. $4500

Answers

A. For example,

Multiplication by 10	Standard form of the number
4 x 10	40
5 x 10	50
8 x 10	80
10 x 10	100

B. For example, each product starts with the number being multiplied by 10 and all end with 1 zero.

C. For example,

Multiplication by 100	Standard form of the number
4 x 100	400
5 x 100	500
8 x 100	800
10 x 100	1000

All of the products start with the number being multiplied by 100 and all end with 2 zeroes.

D. For example,

Multiplication by 1000	Standard form of the number
4 x 1000	4000
5 x 1000	5000
8 x 1000	8000
10 x 1000	10000

Assessment Strategy: written question
Application of Procedures

Question 5
• Multiply a) 99 x 10 b) 5 x 1000 c) 1000 x 10 d) 10 x 1000 e) 15 x 100 f) 100 x 100
(Score correct responses out of 6.)

Extra Practice and Extension

• You might assign any of the questions related to this lesson, which are cross-referenced in the chart below.

Mid-Chapter Review	Student Book p. 40, Question 9
Skills Bank	Student Book p. 49–50, Questions 13, 14 & 15
Problem Bank	Student Book p. 51, Question 6
Chapter Review	Student Book p. 53, Questions 9, 10, 11 & 12
Workbook	p. 15, all questions
Nelson Web Site	Visit www.mathk8.nelson.com and follow the links to *Nelson Mathematics 4*, Chapter 2.

Math Background

As adults, most of us use the strategy of taking a multiplication fact and adding zeros when multiplying by 10, 100, or 1000. However, it is important that students, at this stage, can relate multiplying by those powers of ten to a concrete experience. Base ten blocks and money are good models for this.

It is important to encourage good language. Avoid talk of "adding zeroes" to a number when multiplying by 10 since students have already been taught that when you add zero to a number, the number does not change. Misuse of the word "add" can cause confusion.

At Home

• Students could look for packages of items in supermarkets, toy stores, or catalogues labelled with multiples of 10, 100, or 1000. They can share their findings and create multiplication problems about the packages.

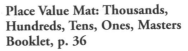

Place Value Mat: Thousands, Hundreds, Tens, Ones, Masters Booklet, p. 36

Mid-Chapter Review

Using Mid-Chapter Review

Use this page to assess students' understanding of the concepts developed in the chapter so far. Refer to the assessment chart on the next page for the details of each question.

Materials: (optional) base ten blocks
Masters: (manipulatives substitute) Base Ten Blocks, Masters Booklet, p. 33-35
(optional) Place Value Mat: Thousands, Hundreds, Tens, Ones, Masters Booklet p. 36

Students may choose to use base ten blocks to help them solve the questions, whether or not the question suggests they do so. Placing blocks or writing digits directly onto a place value chart may also help those students who have difficulty solving any of the questions.

6. Encourage students to use terms such as *place value*, *digit*, *tens place* and so on in their explanations.

Related Questions to Ask

Ask	Possible Response
About **Question 7:** • Because the numbers all have 4 digits, can you explain how you ordered the numbers from least to greatest?	• First I ordered the numbers with the least thousands digit to the greatest. Then I looked at the two numbers that had a 2 in the thousands place. I knew that 2185 had only 1 hundred and 2817 had 8 hundreds, so 2185 is less.
About **Question 9:** • How did the answer to part a) help you solve part b)?	• The answer to part a) tells me that there are 20 hundreds in 2000. I already know there are 10 tens in 1 hundred. That means there must be 20 × 10 tens in 20 hundreds. I can also say this as there are 20 × 10 tens in 2000. Since 20 × 10 = 200, the answer to part b) is 200 tens.

Answers

1. 3 thousands blocks, 7 hundreds blocks, 5 tens blocks

2. 4 thousands + 8 hundreds + 9 ones; 4000 + 800 + 9

3. a) 2085
   b) 6256

4. four hundred sixty-six

5. 4029

CHAPTER 2
Mid-Chapter Review

LESSON

1 1. A blue whale ate 3750 kg of plankton in 1 day. Model 3750 with the least number of blocks possible. Draw the model.

2 2. There are 4809 species of jumping spiders in the world. Write 4809 in expanded form using words and then using numbers.

3. Write each number in standard form.
  a) 2000 + 80 + 5   b) 6 thousands + 2 hundreds + 5 tens + 6 ones

3 4. Use words to write the number that is 100 less than 566.

5. Use numerals to write the number that is three thousand greater than one thousand twenty-nine. Show your work.

6. Complete each number sentence by using <, =, or >. Explain your thinking.
  a) 654 ■ 7843
  b) 9823 ■ 9832
  c) 5478 ■ 8962

7. This table shows the number of dogs of different breeds owned by Canadians. Order the numbers from least to greatest.

Dog	Number
poodle	2817
Yorkshire terrier	2185
boxer	1444
golden retriever	6047
German shepherd	4576

4 8. Complete these number patterns.
  a) 5, ■, 500, 5000
  b) 8 ones, 8 tens, ■, 8 thousands
  c) 4281, 4381, 4481, ■
  d) 1, 10, ■, 1000, ■

5 9. What is the missing number?
  a) 2000 = ■ × 100   c) 5600 = ■ × 100   e) 10 000 = ■ × 100
  b) 2000 = ■ × 10   d) 5600 = ■ × 10   f) 10 000 = ■ × 10

40

NEL

All questions can be used for assessment. (See chart on next page.)

6. a) 654 < 7843; for example, because a 4-digit number is always larger than a 3-digit number

  b) 9823 < 9832; for example, because even though both numbers have the same number of thousands and hundreds, 9832 has more tens.

  c) 5478 < 8962; for example, because 8962 has more thousands than 5478.

7. 1444, 2185, 2817, 4576, 6047

8. a) 50
  b) 8 hundreds
  c) 4581
  d) 100, 10 000

9. a) 20
  b) 200
  c) 56
  d) 560
  e) 100
  f) 1000

Assessment Strategy: written question
Understanding Concepts

Question 1
• A blue whale ate 3750 kg of plankton in 1 day. Model 3750 with the least number of blocks possible. Draw the model.
  (Score 1 point for correct response.)

Assessment Strategy: written question
Communication

Question 2
• There are 4809 species of jumping spiders in the world. Write 4809 in expanded form using words and then using numbers.

Student Name	• 4809 written in expanded form using words is correct (Score 2)	• 4809 written in expanded form using words is partially correct (Score 1)	• 4809 written in expanded form using numbers is correct (Score 2)	• 4809 written in expanded form using numbers is partially correct (Score 1)	Score out of 4
Dylan	2			1	3

Assessment Strategy: written question
Communication

Question 3
• Write each number in standard form.
  a) 2000 + 80 + 5
  b) 6 thousands + 2 hundreds + 5 tens + 6 ones
(Score correct responses out of 2.)

Assessment Strategy: written question
Communication

Question 4
• Use words to write the number that is 100 less than 566.

Student Name	• 466 written using words is correct (Score 2)	• 466 written using words is partially correct (Score 1)	Score out of 2
Carol	2		2

Assessment Strategy: written question
Communication

Question 5
• Use numerals to write the number that is three thousand greater than one thousand twenty-nine. Show your work.

Student Name	• 4029 written in numerals is correct (Score 2)	• 4029 written in numerals is partially correct (Score 1)	• appropriate work is shown (Score 1)	Score out of 3
Claire	2	1		3

Assessment of Learning—What to Look for in Student Work...

Assessment Strategy: written question
Understanding Concepts

Question 6

- Complete each number sentence by using <, =, >. Explain your thinking.
  - a) 654 ■ 7843
  - b) 9823 ■ 9832
  - c) 5478 ■ 8962

(Score 1 point for each ✓ for a total of 6)

Student Name	• number sentence is completed correctly			• provides complete explanation of thinking			Score out of 6
	a)	b)	c)	a)	b)	c)	
Ethan	✓	✓	✓		✓	✓	5

Assessment Strategy: written question
Understanding Concepts

Question 7

- This table shows the number of dogs of different breeds owned by Canadians. Order the numbers from least to greatest.

Student Name	• Re-ordered numbers are correct (Score 2)	• Re-ordered numbers are partially correct (Score 1)	Score out of 2
Brenda	2		2

Assessment Strategy: written question
Application of Procedures

Question 8

- Complete these number patterns.
  - a) 5, ■ 500, 5000
  - b) 8 ones, 8 tens, ■ 8 thousands
  - c) 4281, 4381, 4481, ■
  - d) 1, 10, ■ 1000, ■

(Score correct responses out of 5.)

Assessment Strategy: written question
Application of Procedures

Question 9

- Find the missing number.
  - a) $2000 = ■ \times 100$
  - b) $2000 = ■ \times 10$
  - c) $5600 = ■ \times 100$
  - d) $5600 = ■ \times 10$
  - e) $10\ 000 = ■ \times 100$
  - f) $10\ 000 = ■ \times 10$

(Score correct responses out of 6.)

Math Game: Getting to 10 000

Using the Math Game

Materials: die, game sheet, calculator

Object of the Game

Students multiply numbers they roll with the die by 1, 10, 100, or 1000. After each roll, they add the products. The player with a score that is closest to, but not over, 10 000 wins. The game requires students to use estimating and problem-solving skills to decide by which multiple they should multiply the number they've rolled. They also use estimating or mental math skills as the game progresses to determine the difference between their running totals and 10 000.

When to Play

Students can play this game after they demonstrate a good understanding of the concepts of multiplying by 10, 100, and 1000. Students should also have a good sense of how big 10 000 is in relation to groups of thousands, hundreds, tens, and ones. Play can begin anytime after Lesson 5.

Strategies

Some students may choose to start the game by multiplying all the numbers they roll by 1000 to get as close to 10 000 as quickly as possible. Then they multiply by 100, 10, or 1, basing their choice of which multiple to use on the number they've rolled and on their running total. Other students may choose a mixture of multiplying by 1000, 100, 10, or 1 for about the first half of the game and then try to narrow in as they get closer to 10 000.

This game involves "luck of the roll" to some extent. This is more apparent near the end of the 10 rolls when a student who has a running total close to 10 000 hopes to roll a low number on the die, while a student with a lower running total hopes to roll a higher number on the die.

Observe

Watch for students who do the following:

- mentally add the product determined by each roll to their running total
- mentally determine how much they need to get close to, but not go over, 10 000
- decide which multiple to use (1000, 100, 10, or 1) without any reason

Conduct participatory observation by playing a game with a student. Watch for students who are using a strategy and are able to explain what they are doing.

Discuss

Throughout the game, ask students the following:

- What is your running total right now? How much more do you need to reach 10 000?
- What number would you like to roll next on the die?

After the game, ask students the following:

- What strategy did you use to help you decide whether to use 1000, 100, 10, or 1 to multiply by?

- Did you have a strategy when you began playing the game?
- Did you change your strategy as the game went along?

Variations

- A simpler version: Students could play "Getting to 1000." The game is played the same way, but students choose to multiply by 100, 10, or 1. The first player to get closest to 1000, without going over, after 10 rolls wins.
- For students experiencing difficulty: Students could use base ten blocks to model each product (their roll multiplied by 1000, 100, 10, or 1). They could tally their running total with base ten blocks, regrouping blocks as necessary. The first player to get 10 thousand blocks wins.

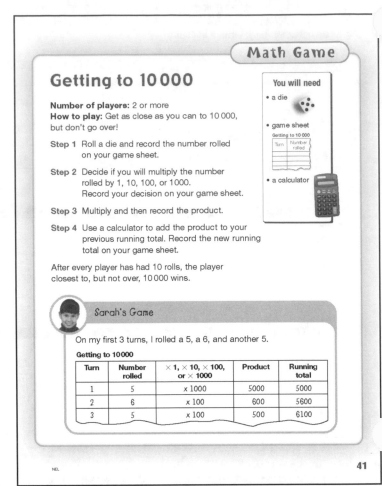

Math Game

Getting to 10 000

Number of players: 2 or more
How to play: Get as close as you can to 10 000, but don't go over!

Step 1 Roll a die and record the number rolled on your game sheet.

Step 2 Decide if you will multiply the number rolled by 1, 10, 100, or 1000. Record your decision on your game sheet.

Step 3 Multiply and then record the product.

Step 4 Use a calculator to add the product to your previous running total. Record the new running total on your game sheet.

After every player has had 10 rolls, the player closest to, but not over, 10 000 wins.

You will need
- a die
- game sheet
- a calculator

Sarah's Game

On my first 3 turns, I rolled a 5, a 6, and another 5.

Getting to 10 000

Turn	Number rolled	× 1, × 10, × 100, or × 1000	Product	Running total
1	5	x 1000	5000	5000
2	6	x 100	600	5600
3	5	x 100	500	6100

NEL

41

6 Rounding to the Nearest 10, 100, or 1000

Goal Round numbers to the nearest 10, 100 or 1000.

Prerequisite Skills/Concepts

- Compare and order whole numbers to 10 000.

Expectations

4m15 represent and explain number concepts and procedures
4m17 identify and appreciate the use of numbers in the media

Assessment for Feedback	What You Will See Students Doing...	
Students will	**When Students Understand**	**If Students Misunderstand**
• compare and order whole numbers to 10 000	• Students will be able to compare a given number to two other numbers that the first number is between and tell which of the two numbers it is closer to.	• Students may make mistakes about which numbers to use on a number line. The place value that students are asked to round to will tell them which numbers to write near each end (e.g., if they are rounding to the nearest 100, they write the number with the next highest 100 and the number with the next lowest 100 on the number line). You may wish to use the example on pp. 42–43 and incorporate all three roundings on one number line.

Preparation and Planning

Pacing	**5–10 min** Introduction **10–15 min** Teaching and Learning **25–35 min** Consolidation
Materials	• (optional) number cards labelled 7000 and 8000
Resources	• (Mental Math p. 60 • (for Extra Support) Number Lines, Masters Booklet, p. 32 • (for Extra Support of Question 4) Scaffolding, p. 68
Workbook	p. 16
Key Assessment of Learning Question	Question 4, Understanding of Concepts, Communication

Meeting Individual Needs

Extra Challenge

- Write a 4-digit number on the board. Ask some students to round to the nearest 10, others to round it to the nearest 100, and others to the nearest 1000. Compare the results. Challenge students with numbers such as the following: 1999, 2004, 2449, and 2450. Compare the results.

Extra Support

- Use the Number Lines Master to work through examples of rounding with those students who require extra practice. It is best if you number each of the marks representing numbers on the number line so that students can see exactly how a particular number is closer to one number than another.

1. Introduction (Whole Class)
▶ 5–10 min

Make an over-sized number line by writing the numbers 7000 and 8000 on opposite ends of the board. (Alternatively, you can have two students stand at opposite ends of the classroom and hold up number cards with 7000 and 8000 written on them). Call out a number (e.g., 7783), and ask a student to write that number on the number line in the approximate position where it should go or stand between the two students holding cards).

Talk about which number 7783 is closer to: 7000 or 8000. Ask students to tell you how they know that 7783 is closer to 8000. Explain that this is called rounding to the nearest thousand.

Ask students to tell you what number they think is exactly in the middle of 7000 and 8000.

Repeat with other 4-digit numbers between 7000 and 8000.

Sample Discourse

"How do you know 7783 is closer to 8000?"
- *I looked at the hundreds. 7783 has 7 hundreds. That's 700 away from 7000 but only 300 away from 8000.*

"How do you know which numbers are closer to 7000 and which to 8000?"
- *Any number between 7000 and 8000 with less than 5 hundreds is closer to 7000. Any number between 7000 and 8000 with more than 5 hundreds is closer to 8000.*

Tell students they are going to round numbers to the nearest 10 and 100.

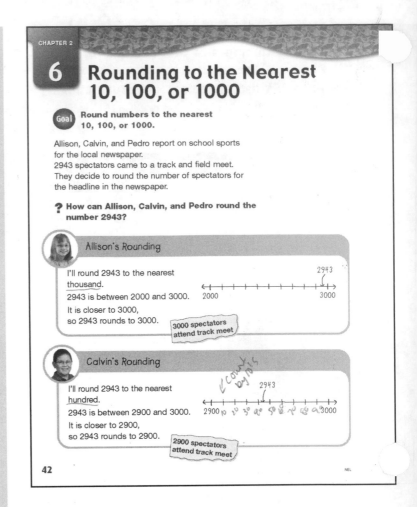

2. Teaching and Learning (Whole Class) ▶ 10–15 min

Ask a student to read the example at the top of p. 42. Draw attention to the central question. Compare how Allison rounded to the nearest thousand to how the students rounded to the nearest thousand using their over-sized number line. Ask students to identify what they did the same as and what they did differently from Allison. Then discuss Calvin's and Pedro's rounding. Talk about how rounding to the nearest hundred and the nearest ten are the same as and different from rounding to the nearest thousand.

Sample Discourse

"How did Calvin round to the nearest hundred?"
- *First he had to find out which two numbers with even hundreds 2943 was between. The numbers are 2900 and 3000. Then he had to find out whether it was closer to 2900 or 3000.*

"How did Calvin know that 2943 is closer to 2900?
- *2943 has 4 tens so it is about 40 away from 2900 and about 60 away from 3000. It is closer to 2900.*

Reflecting

Use these questions to ensure that students understand that the process for rounding to the nearest 10, 100, or 1000 is the same in that for each, the student looks at the place values with even numbers of the given unit (i.e., the unit they are rounding to) both less than and greater than the number (e.g., when rounding to the nearest 100, they look at the even hundreds just less than and just greater than the number). They then decide which of those two numbers the number is closer to. Discuss the questions, encouraging various responses.

Sample Discourse

1. • *3000 is best because 2943 is very close to 3020.*
   • *3000 is best because it gives you a general idea of how many people were at the track and field meet.*

2. • *It's different because you compare hundreds instead of thousands.*
   • *It's different because when you round to the nearest 1000 you get 2000, but when you round to the nearest 100, you get 1700.*

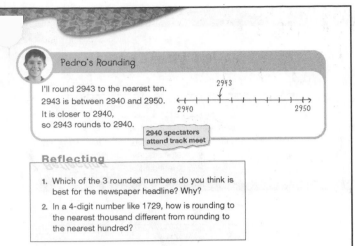

Pedro's Rounding

I'll round 2943 to the nearest ten.
2943 is between 2940 and 2950.
It is closer to 2940,
so 2943 rounds to 2940.

2943

2940   2950

2940 spectators attend track meet

Reflecting

1. Which of the 3 rounded numbers do you think is best for the newspaper headline? Why?

2. In a 4-digit number like 1729, how is rounding to the nearest thousand different from rounding to the nearest hundred?

Checking

3. There were 4365 spectators at a provincial softball championship. Round 4365 to the nearest thousand, the nearest hundred, and the nearest ten.

Practising

4. a) Draw a number line to show how you would round the population of Fergus to the nearest thousand.
   b) What is the population of Pelee rounded to the nearest hundred? What is Pelee's population rounded to the nearest ten?
   c) What community has about 3000 people?
   d) Explain why the populations of Mount Forest, Petrolia, and Gananoque are all about 5000 when rounded to the nearest thousand.

Place	Population
Fergus	8884
Pelee	283
Kincardine	2954
Mount Forest	4580
Petrolia	4908
Gananoque	5210

NEL

43

3. Consolidation ▶ 25–35 min

Checking (Small Groups)

For intervention strategies, refer to the Meeting Individual Needs box or the Assessment for Feedback chart.

Students may wish to use the Number Lines Master to help them round.

Practising (Individual)

4. If students require Extra Support for **Question 4**, provide them with copies of **Scaffolding Master p. 68.** Ask students to explain their thinking as they work through these problems.

4. **d)** Students' explanations will be a strong indication of their understanding of rounding to different place values within a 4-digit number.

Related Questions to Ask

Ask	Possible Responses
About **Question 3:** • Ask students to think about why the number of spectators might be rounded to the nearest 1000, the nearest 100, and the nearest 10.	• A newspaper might round the attendance to the nearest 1000. People who sell hot dogs at the game might round to the nearest 100. People who sell tickets to the game might round to the nearest 10.

Closing (Whole Class)

Have students summarize their learning by asking the students to work in groups of 3. Each student takes turns choosing one way to round 4575 (i.e., to the nearest 1000, 100, or 10) and explain to the other two students how the rounding was done.

Answers

1. For example, the number rounded to the nearest thousand is best because it gives a good approximation of how many people were there.

2. For example, when rounding to the nearest thousand, you are deciding whether 1729 is closer to 1000 or 2000. It is closer to 2000. When rounding to the nearest hundred, you are deciding whether 1729 is closer to 1700 or 1800. It is closer to 1700.

3. 4000, 4400, 4370

4. a)

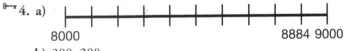

8000   8884 9000

   b) 300, 280

   c) Kincardine

   d) 4580 and 4908 are both closer to 5000 than to 4000. Even though 5210 is greater than 5000, it is still closer to 5000 than to 6000.

Assessment Strategy: written question
Communication

Question 4 a)
• Draw a number line to show how you would round the population of Fergus to the nearest thousand.

1	2	3	4
• uses a number line that exhibits minimal clarity and accuracy, and is ineffective in communicating the process of rounding	• uses a number line that lacks either clarity or accuracy, though not sufficient to impede communication of the process of rounding	• uses a number line that is sufficiently clear and accurate to communicate the process of rounding	• uses a number line that is clear, precise, and effective in communicating the process of rounding

Assessment Strategy: written question
Understanding Concepts

Question 4 b)
What is the population of Pelee rounded to the nearest hundred? What is Pelee's population rounded to the nearest ten?
Question 4 c)
What community has about 3000 people?
(Score correct responses to b) and c) out of 3.)

Assessment Strategy: written question
Communication

Question 4 d)
• Explain why the populations of Mount Forest, Petrolia, and Gananoque are all about 5000 when rounded to the nearest thousand.

1	2	3	4
• provides incomplete or inaccurate justification for rounding the numbers to 5000	• provides partial justification for rounding the numbers to 5000	• provides a clear and logical justification for rounding the numbers to 5000	• provides a thorough, clear, and insightful justification for rounding the numbers to 5000

Extra Practice and Extension

• You might assign any of the questions related to this lesson, which are cross-referenced in the chart below.

Skills Bank	Student Book p. 50, Questions 16, 17, & 18
Problem Bank	Student Book p. 51, Question 7
Chapter Review	Student Book p. 53, Questions 13, 14, & 15
Workbook	p. 16, all questions
Nelson Web Site	Visit www.mathk8.nelson.com and follow the links to *Nelson Mathematics 4*, Chapter 2.

Math Background

In real life situations, we do not always round to the nearest power of ten (e.g., when dealing with money). For this grade level, however, rounding to the nearest 10 is a reasonable place to start.

Although some people use fairly rigid rounding rules (e.g., always round up if a digit is 5), it is best to promote some flexibility (e.g., when adding 45 + 55, it makes sense to round one down and the other up to get a sum closer to the actual value).

At Home

• Students could answer questions involving numbers in their daily lives that they can round. For example, "About how much will that cost?" "About how far is it to my friend's house?"

Extra Support: Number Lines, Masters Booklet p. 32

7

Communicate About Ordering Numbers

Goal Explain how to order a set of numbers in a complete, clear, and organized way.

Prerequisite Skills/Concepts

- Compare and order whole numbers to 10 000.

Expectations

4m2	compare and order whole numbers (and decimals) using concrete materials and drawings
4m13	compare and order whole numbers (and decimals from 0.01) to 10 000 using concrete materials, drawings, and symbols
4m15	represent and explain number concepts and procedures
4m32	explain their thinking when solving problems involving whole numbers

Assessment for Feedback	What You Will See Students Doing...	
Students will	**When Students Understand**	**If Students Misunderstand**
• compare and order numbers to 10 000	• Students will be able to explain why one 3-digit or 4-digit number is greater or less than another.	• Some students may be able to compare numbers correctly, but are not able to explain why one is greater than or less than another. Have these students use base ten blocks to help them visualize how one number is larger than another as they attempt to explain it in words.
• represent and explain number concepts and procedures	• Students will be able to use mathematical language such as *digit*, *place value*, *greater than*, and *less than* to describe a set of numbers.	• Some students may try to describe sets of numbers using ambiguous language (e.g., "This number is bigger than that number" or "There are more numbers in this number"). Prompt students to use more precise mathematical language such as *digit* and *place value* instead of the ambiguous language.

Preparation and Planning

Pacing	5–10 min Introduction 10–15 min Teaching and Learning 25–35 min Consolidation
Materials	• (for Extra Challenge) several sets of number cards 0–9 • (for Extra Support) base ten blocks (ones, tens, hundreds, and thousands)
Resources	• Mental Math, p. 60 • (manipulatives substitute) Base Ten Blocks, Masters Booklet, pp. 33-35
Workbook	p. 17
Key Assessment of Learning Question	Question 3, Understanding of Concepts, Communication

Meeting Individual Needs

Extra Challenge

- Students can take four cards from sets of number cards labelled 0–9. Using the 4 digits they've drawn, students can create four different 4-digit numbers and order them from least to greatest. They can then explain how they ordered them.

Extra Support

- Students may benefit from using base ten blocks to model the numbers in a set of numbers they are to order. The blocks enable them to visualize the number and type of block used to make each number. This visualization can help them focus on terms such as *place value* and *hundreds digit* when writing their explanation for ordering.

1. Introduction (Whole Class)
▶ 5–10 min

Present the students with a variety of numbers and ask them to explain how they would put them in order.

Sample Discourse

"How would you put the numbers 7, 295, 8290, and 36 in order from greatest to least?"
• *8290, 295, 36, 7*

"How did you know which order to put them in?"
• *I put the 4-digit number first because it was the greatest, then the 3-digit number, then the 2-digit one, and then the 1-digit one.*

"How would you put the numbers 764, 492, 2005, and 6321 in order from greatest to least?"
• *The 4-digit numbers are greater than the 3-digit ones, so I put them first. 6321 has more thousands than 2005 so it comes before 2005. 764 has more hundreds than 492 so it comes before 492. 492 goes last.*

Repeat with more sets of numbers. Tell students that they are going to put sets of numbers in order and explain in a complete, clear, and organized way how they ordered the numbers.

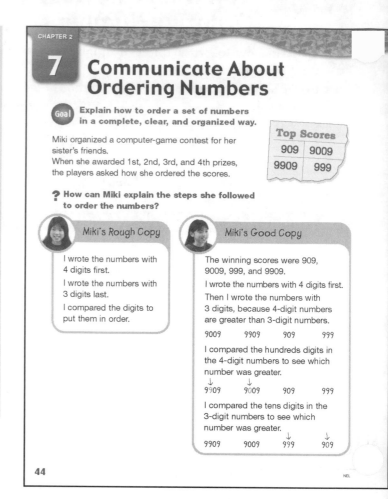

2. Teaching and Learning (Pairs) ▶ 10–15 min

Ask students to look at the Top Scores at the top of p. 44 and to explain to a partner how they would put the numbers in order. Draw attention to the central question. Tell students to read Miki's Rough Copy of her explanation of how she ordered the numbers and have them work in pairs to evaluate it. They should use the Communication Checklist from the top of p. 45:

• Did Miki show all the steps?

• Did Miki explain her thinking?

Students can continue working with their partner to read Miki's Good Copy of her explanation, again using the Communication Checklist to evaluate the explanation.

You may wish to record the points from the Communication Checklist on a class chart. Post it so it is clearly visible to students, and so you can add new points as you come to them with subsequent communication lessons. Here are some additional points to add for this lesson:

• Did you put the steps in order?

• Did you show the right amount of detail?

• Did you include an example or a diagram?

• Did you use math language?

Reflecting

Discuss the question, encouraging various responses. Remind students that it is important to use math language, show all their steps, and explain their thinking clearly and with detail.

Sample Discourse

1. • *Miki didn't show all her steps in her rough copy because there are two 4-digit numbers and two 3-digit numbers and Miki didn't say how she would order those. In her good copy, Miki showed all her steps and she put the steps in the right order.*

   • *Miki didn't say in her rough copy which digits she compared, but in her good copy, she used arrows to point to the digits she was talking about.*

   • *Miki used math language like "4-digit numbers" and "hundreds digit" in her good copy.*

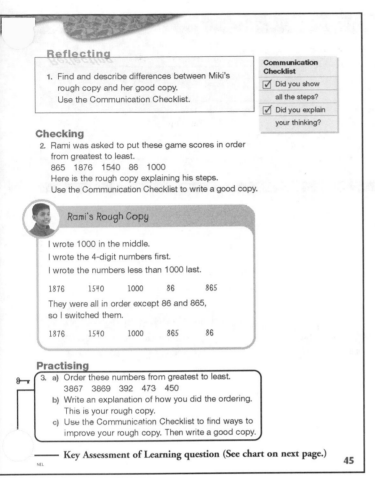

Reflecting

1. Find and describe differences between Miki's rough copy and her good copy. Use the Communication Checklist.

Checking

2. Rami was asked to put these game scores in order from greatest to least.
865 1876 1540 86 1000
Here is the rough copy explaining his steps.
Use the Communication Checklist to write a good copy.

> **Rami's Rough Copy**
>
> I wrote 1000 in the middle.
> I wrote the 4-digit numbers first.
> I wrote the numbers less than 1000 last.
>
> 1876   1540   1000   86   865
>
> They were all in order except 86 and 865, so I switched them.
>
> 1876   1540   1000   865   86

Practising

3. a) Order these numbers from greatest to least.
   3867 3869 392 473 450
   b) Write an explanation of how you did the ordering. This is your rough copy.
   c) Use the Communication Checklist to find ways to improve your rough copy. Then write a good copy.

—— **Key Assessment of Learning question** (See chart on next page.)

45

---

3. Consolidation ▸ 25–35 min

Checking (Small Groups)

For intervention strategies, refer to the Meeting Individual Needs box or the Assessment for Feedback chart.

2. Encourage students to use the Communication Checklist on p. 45 to write a good copy for Rami. Students can also be directed to use Miki's good copy on p. 44 as an example of how much detail they should show.

Practising (Individual)

3. **b)** While students may be able to order the number easily, they may have some difficulty explaining how they did it. Encourage them to write one or more rough copies before attempting a good copy.

c) Students can also use Miki's good copy as a model to follow as they write their good copy.

Closing (Whole Class)

Have students summarize their learning by displaying the following numbers and asking, "How can you explain the steps you followed to order the numbers from greatest to least?"
  6532, 362, 273, 5623
Students may write their explanations in a journal entry.

Answers

1. For example, in the rough copy, Miki didn't explain much of her thinking, but in the good copy, she explained why she wrote the 4-digit numbers before the 3-digit numbers, and she showed how she compared the hundreds digits and the tens digits.

2. For example, I had to put the numbers 865, 1876, 1540, 86, and 1000 in order. I knew that some of the numbers were more than 1000 and some were less, so I wrote 1000 in the middle. I wrote the 4-digit numbers before 1000 and the smaller numbers after 1000: 1876, 1540, 1000, 86, 865. I then compared the hundreds digits of the numbers more than 1000:
   1⑧76 1⑤40
   The numbers were in the right order because 8 is greater than 5. 86 and 865 were easy to compare because 86 is less than 100 and 865 is greater than 100. So 865 came before 86. Then I wrote all the numbers in order from greatest to least: 1876 1540 1000 865 86

3. **a)** 3869, 3867, 473, 450, 392
   b) For example, I knew 3867 and 3869 were the biggest numbers because they have 4 digits. I wrote the one with 9 ones first.
   3869 3867

I knew the one with 3 hundreds was the smallest number so I left a space and wrote it on the right.
3869 3867   392
I only had 473 and 450 left, so I wrote them in the middle.
3869 3867 473 450 392

c) For example, I was asked to order the numbers 3867, 3869, 392, 473, and 450. I knew 3867 and 3869 were the biggest numbers because they have 4 digits. I then compared the ones digits: 9 is greater than 7, so 3869 is greater than 3867:
   386⑨ 386⑦
I knew the number with 3 hundreds was the smallest number because the other 3-digit numbers have 4 hundreds. I left a space after 3867 so I would have room to write the numbers with 4 hundreds and then I wrote 392.
3869 3867 392
I only had 473 and 450 left. They both have 4 hundreds but I know that 73 is more than 50 so I wrote 473 first and 450 second. I put both numbers in the space between 3867 and 392.
3869 3867 473 450   392

Assessment Strategy: written question
Understanding Concepts

Question 3 a)
• Order these numbers from greatest to least: 3867 3869 392 473 450

Student Name	numbers are in correct order (score 2)	numbers are in partially correct order (score 1)	Total out of 2
Beverley		1	1
Gary	2		2

Assessment Strategy: written question
Communication

Question 3 b)
• Write an explanation of how you did the ordering.
Question 3 c)
• Use the Communication Checklist to find ways to improve your rough copy. Then write a good copy.

1	2	3	4
• provides incomplete or inaccurate explanations that lack clarity or logical thought using very little mathematical vocabulary	• provides partial explanation that exhibits some clarity and logical thought using a limited range of mathematical vocabulary	• provides complete, clear and logical explanation using mathematical vocabulary	• provides thorough, clear and insightful explanation using a broad range of mathematical vocabulary

Extra Practice and Extension

• You might assign any of the questions related to this lesson, which are cross-referenced in the chart below.

Workbook	p. 17, all questions
Nelson Web Site	Visit www.mathk8.nelson.com and follow the links to *Nelson Mathematics 4*, Chapter 2.

At Home

• Students could gather real data from newspapers, order the numbers, and explain how they ordered them. Examples of real data could be sports scores or sale prices listed in advertisements.

Math Background

It is important that students learn to explain their thinking in a clear and organized way. This is not particularly easy for many students. Although they may be able to do the math involved in ordering sets of numbers, they may have difficulty explaining clearly how they ordered the numbers. Through practice and by emphasizing the use of math language and detail, these explanations should become easier for students to write. The concept of a rough copy and good copy, although familiar in language arts, may be a new idea for some students in math.

Counting Money Collections

Goal **Estimate, count, and write money amounts up to $50.00.**

Prerequisite Skills/Concepts

- Read and write money amounts using the dollar sign and decimal format (e.g., $0.89).
- Estimate, count, and record the value in collections of coins and bills to $10.
- Demonstrate the relationship between all coins and bills up to $100.

Expectations

4m47 read and write money values to $50

4m48 estimate the amount of money in collections of coins and bills to $50 and count to determine the total value

Assessment for Feedback	What You Will See Students Doing...	
Students will	**When Students Understand**	**If Students Misunderstand**
• read and write money to $50 using the dollar sign and decimal format	• Students will read and write money amounts correctly, referring to the numbers to the left of the decimal as dollars and numbers to the right of the decimal as cents. Students will always place at least 1 digit to the left of the decimal and 2 digits to the right of the decimal	• Students may place the dollar sign to the right of the amount or draw the dollar sign incorrectly (e.g., as a backwards S). Review with students that, in our money system, the dollar sign is always placed to the left of the amount. Some students may need paper and pencil practice to correctly draw the dollar sign.
• estimate, count, and record in a collection of coins and bills the value up to $50 and demonstrate the relationship between all coins and bills up to $100	• Students can estimate, then correctly count and record, the value of a collection of coins and bills up to $50. They are able to explain their strategy for estimating and counting and they can demonstrate correctly the relationship between all coins and bills up to $100.	• Students may not know the value of each of the coins and bills. They may not know the relationships between some of the coins and bills. Play a simple game or activity that involves trading and counting money such as Race to a Toonie (see Extra Support).

Preparation and Planning

Pacing	**5–10 min** Introduction **10–15 min** Teaching and Learning **25–35 min** Consolidation
Materials	• play money (bills and coins)
Masters	• Mental Math, p. 60
Resources	• (for Extra Support) Place Value Mat: Hundreds, Tens, Ones, Masters Booklet, p. 37
Workbook	p. 18
Vocabulary/ Symbols	dollars, cents, dollar sign, decimal, bills, toonie, loonie, quarter, dime, nickel, penny
Key Assessment of Learning Question	Question 6, Understanding of Concepts

Meeting Individual Needs

Extra Challenge

- Challenge students to use the least number of bills and coins possible to make the amounts of money collected by Paulette's class each day.
- Present students with various money amounts up to $50. Have students use bills and coins to make each amount in two different ways. Tell them that one of the two ways must use the least number of bills and coins possible.

Extra Support

- Some students may need additional practice trading coins of less than a dollar's value up to a loonie. Review with these students the following coin equivalencies:
  - 1 loonie = 100 pennies = 10 dimes = 20 nickels = 4 quarters
  - 1 quarter = 2 dimes and a nickel
- To reinforce writing money amounts, you may wish to use loonies, dimes, and pennies and a place value chart labelled with a $ sign and decimal. Students can place the coins directly on the chart and then write in the amounts.

1. Introduction (Whole Class)
▶ 5–10 min

Use a box filled with play coins, including pennies, nickels, dimes, quarters, loonies, and toonies. Ask a student to scoop out as many coins as possible using one hand. Have the other students estimate how much money is in the student's hand. Ask students for suggestions as to how to count the money exactly. Repeat with students taking turns scooping up the coins. Then repeat with students scooping coins with both hands. Estimate and then count the money each time.

Sample Discourse

"How much money do you think Nicky has scooped out?"
- *I think about $2.60.*

"How did you estimate that amount?"
- *I saw a couple of loonies in her hand and maybe 2 quarters and lots of pennies, so I thought it was probably about $2.60.*

"How can we count Nicky's money?"
- *I'd start with the loonies. Then I'd see if I can count up any of the other coins so that I can trade them for a loonie. If not, I'd just count up the money starting with the quarters, then the dimes, then the nickels, and then the pennies.*

Encourage students to share their estimating and counting strategies. While there is not one correct way to count money, there are ways that are more efficient.

Tell students they are going to estimate and count money amounts easily and quickly.

---

8 Counting Money Collections

You will need
- play money

Goal Estimate, count, and write money amounts up to $50.00.

The class is fund-raising for a camping trip.
Paulette is the class treasurer.
She records how much money is collected each day.

Day 1	Day 2	Day 3	Day 4
3 five-dollar bills	1 toonie	1 five-dollar bill	1 five-dollar bill
5 loonies	2 quarters	2 toonies	1 toonie
3 quarters	10 dimes	4 quarters	5 loonies
5 dimes	3 nickels	5 dimes	18 nickels
2 nickels	10 pennies	2 nickels	50 pennies
5 pennies		80 pennies	

? How much money has Paulette's class collected?

Paulette's Estimate

First, I will estimate the total for each day.
When I write number values, the number before the decimal tells how many dollars.
The number after the decimal tells how many cents.

Day	Estimate
1	$21.00
2	$4.00
3	$11.00
4	$13.00

---

2. Teaching and Learning (Whole Class) ▶ 10–15 min

Ask a student to read the sentences at the top of p. 46. Have play money available to show students the exact amount of money collected on Day 1. Ask how Paulette might have arrived at her estimate of $21.00. Then ask students how they could count this amount of money exactly. Draw attention to the central question and use the play money to repeat the estimating for Days 2, 3 and 4. Add the estimates for each day together to estimate the total amount collected.

Ask students how they might calculate the actual total. Be prepared to accept different methods for calculating this total. Ask students to explain their thinking. Some students may simply add the exact totals for the days in a column addition. Other students may suggest physically grouping like bills and coins and trading up to find the total (e.g., trading each set of 4 quarters for loonies, etc.).

Reflecting

Use these questions to ensure that students understand their own method for estimating and counting and to determine whether it is an efficient method. By sharing methods with each other, some students may find a more efficient method than their own. Discuss the questions, encouraging various responses.

Sample Discourse

1. • *My actual total was only $0.95 more than my estimate. That's pretty close so my estimate was reasonable.*
   • *My actual total was $3.50 more than my estimate, so my estimate wasn't very good. I estimated too high.*

2. • *I added up the actual totals for each day, then added each day's total together to get the actual total.*
   • *I added up all the bills first, then all the toonies, then all the loonies. Then I figured out how many quarters there were and traded them for loonies. I added up all the dimes and traded them for loonies too. Then I counted the nickels, then the pennies, and then I added that amount to the amount of dollars I had counted.*

A. Add the estimates for each day together to estimate the total amount collected.

B. Calculate the actual total.

Reflecting

1. Compare your estimate with your actual total. Is your actual total reasonable?

2. Share your method for finding the actual total with others. Why were some methods different?

Checking

3. On day 5 of fund-raising, Paulette's class collected this amount.
   a) Estimate how much money the class raised.
   b) Calculate the actual total for day 5.

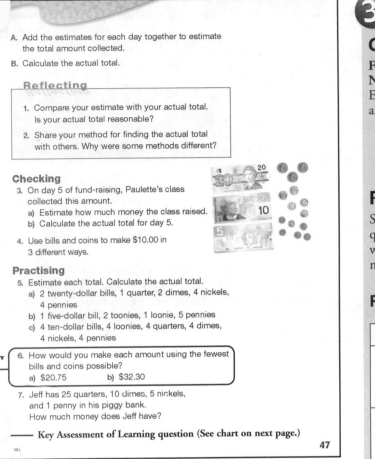

4. Use bills and coins to make $10.00 in 3 different ways.

Practising

5. Estimate each total. Calculate the actual total.
   a) 2 twenty-dollar bills, 1 quarter, 2 dimes, 4 nickels, 4 pennies
   b) 1 five-dollar bill, 2 toonies, 1 loonie, 5 pennies
   c) 4 ten-dollar bills, 4 loonies, 4 quarters, 4 dimes, 4 nickels, 4 pennies

6. How would you make each amount using the fewest bills and coins possible?
   a) $20.75   b) $32.30

7. Jeff has 25 quarters, 10 dimes, 5 nickels, and 1 penny in his piggy bank. How much money does Jeff have?

— **Key Assessment of Learning question (See chart on next page.)**

Checking (Small Groups)

For intervention strategies, refer to the Meeting Individual Needs box or the Assessment for Feedback chart.
Encourage students to share their methods for estimating and counting the money collected on Day 5.

4. Ask students to choose which of their three suggestions is the easiest way to make $10.00 (one $10 bill).

Practising (Individual)

Some students may need to use play money to answer the questions. Seeing the money may help students to estimate, while physically manipulating and trading coins and bills may help them to find actual totals.

Related Questions to Ask

Ask	Possible Response
About **Question 5:** • Can each of these money amounts be made using other bills and coins?	• *Yes, I can trade bills and coins. I can trade 2 toonies and 1 loonie for a five-dollar bill.*
About **Question 7:** • Can you make the amount in Jeff's piggy bank using bills and coins?	• *I could use a five-dollar bill, a toonie, 2 quarters, and a penny.*

Closing (Whole Class)

Have students summarize their learning by having them take turns telling how they could make $20.75 using bills and coins. Encourage each student to come up with two ways.

Answers

A. $47.00

B. $47.95

1. For example, my estimate was very close so it is reasonable.

2. For example, I started by counting the bills, the toonies, and the loonies, and then I worked my way down to the other coins. I counted the quarters first by trading each 4 quarters for a dollar. I did the same for the other coins. There are many ways to count money because the order in which you add doesn't change the final amount.

3. **a)** For example, about $40   **b)** $41.98

4. For example,
   • 2 $5 bills
   • 1 $5 bill, 2 toonies, 1 loonie
   • 1 $10 bill

5. **a)** For example, $41.00; $40.69
   b) For example, $8.00; $8.05
   c) For example, $45.00; $45.64

6. **a)** one $20 bill, 3 quarters
   b) one $20 bill, one $10 bill, 1 toonie, 1 quarter, 1 nickel

7. $7.51

Assessment of Learning—What to Look for in Student Work...

Assessment Strategy: written question
Understanding Concepts

Question 6
• How would you make each amount using the fewest bills and coins possible? a) $20.75 b) $32.30

Student Name	• representation of the amount using bills and coins is correct (Score 2)		• representation of the amount using bills and coins is partially correct (i.e., bills and coins are not the fewest possible) (Score 1)		Score out of 6
	a)	b)	a)	b)	
Gwen	2			1	3

Extra Practice and Extension

• You might assign any of the questions related to this lesson, which are cross-referenced in the chart below.

Skills Bank	Student Book p. 50, Questions 19 & 20
Problem Bank	Student Book p. 51, Questions 8 & 9
Chapter Review	Student Book p. 53, Questions 16 & 17
Workbook	p. 18, all questions
Nelson Web Site	Visit www.mathk8.nelson.com and follow the links to *Nelson Mathematics 4*, Chapter 2.

At Home

• Students could count real money with their family members in real-life situations, such as buying groceries.
• Students could use real money to model different prices from flyers they receive at home from local pharmacies or supermarkets.

Math Background

This lesson focuses on how to efficiently count collections of money. The underlying two ideas are that students should group like amounts, and they should start with the largest denominations and work down.

This is parallel to counting a set of base ten blocks in which students start with the hundreds and group them into sets of tens to count efficiently. Although there are aspects of working with money that relate to the place value system that is the focus of this chapter, there are aspects of dealing with money that do not fit as neatly into our system for writing numbers.

For example, students have learned that there are various ways to represent 124: 1 hundreds, 2 tens, and 4 ones, or 12 tens and 4 ones, or 11 tens and 14 ones, or 10 tens and 24 ones, and so on. Similarly, 1 loonie, 2 dimes, and 4 pennies can be represented as 12 dimes and 4 pennies, or 11 dimes and 14 pennies, and so on. But when nickels and quarters are used, the number of possible groupings increases even more. Students learn to group nickels and quarters as well as dimes and pennies to make counting more efficient.

Place Value Mat: Hundreds, Tens, Ones, Masters Booklet, p. 37

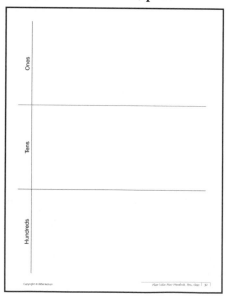

Skills Bank

Using the Skills Bank

Materials: base ten blocks, play money (bills and coins)
Students may choose to use base ten blocks to help them
solve the questions, whether or not the question suggests
they do so.

2. The least number of blocks used for modelling numbers
   is directly related to the number in expanded form. If
   students are having difficulty with this question, have
   them write out the number in expanded form.

10. You may want to ask students which languages are
    missing and why. (English and French are missing
    because more than 10 000 people in Ottawa-Hull
    speak them as their first language.)

19. & 20. Some students may need to physically
          manipulate play money to determine
          the answers.

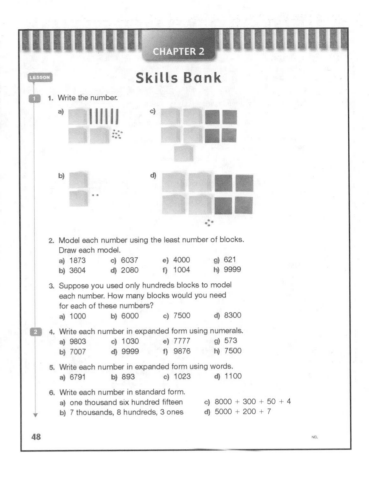

Answers

1. **a)** 3069 **b)** 2002 **c)** 5400 **d)** 4404

2. **a)** 1 thousands block, 8 hundreds blocks, 7 tens blocks,
   3 ones blocks

   b) 3 thousands blocks, 6 hundreds blocks, 4 ones blocks

   c) 6 thousands blocks, 3 tens blocks, 7 ones blocks

   d) 2 thousands blocks, 8 tens blocks

   e) 4 thousands blocks

   f) 1 thousands block, 4 ones blocks

   g) 6 hundreds blocks, 2 tens blocks, 1 ones block

   h) 9 thousands blocks, 9 hundreds blocks, 9 tens blocks,
   9 ones blocks

3. **a)** 10 **b)** 60 **c)** 75 **d)** 83

4. **a)** 9000 + 800 + 3 **b)** 7000 + 7 **c)** 1000 + 30

   d) 9000 + 900 + 90 + 9 **e)** 7000 + 700 + 70 + 7

   f) 9000 + 800 + 70 + 6 **g)** 500 + 70 + 3

   h) 7000 + 500

5. **a)** 6 thousands + 7 hundreds + 9 tens + 1 one

   b) 8 hundreds + 9 tens + 3 ones

   c) 1 thousand + 2 tens + 3 ones

   d) 1 thousand + 1 hundred

6. **a)** 1615 **b)** 7803 **c)** 8354 **d)** 5207

7. Complete each number sentence by using <, =, or >.
   a) 986 ■ 953   d) 10 000 ■ 1000   g) 559 ■ 5590
   b) 2234 ■ 2432   e) 9909 ■ 9990   h) 1342 ■ 1351
   c) 7629 ■ 983   f) 7685 ■ 7658   i) 3980 ■ 4995

8. Order each set of numbers from least to greatest.
   a) 8561, 7982, 8642, 693   c) 7982, 7984, 7992, 7899
   b) 9805, 3248, 653, 3379, 3241   d) 543, 5672, 9870, 5070, 9930

9. Use each set of digits to write four 4-digit numbers.
   Order the numbers from least to greatest.
   a) 7, 9, 9, 0   b) 2, 4, 4, 8   c) 1, 3, 5, 0

10. The table shows the number of people in Ottawa-Hull who speak each language as their first language.
    a) Which language is spoken by the greatest number of people?
    b) Which language is spoken by the least number of people?
    c) Write the numbers from greatest to least.

First language	Number of people
Dutch	3055
German	7455
Greek	2325
Polish	6495
Portuguese	6345
Spanish	9020

11. Complete each number pattern.
    a) 7, ■, 700, 7000   d) 4682, 5682, 6682, ■, ■
    b) 4997, 4998, 4999, ■, ■   e) 683, 783, 883, ■, ■
    c) 8719, 8723, 8727, ■, ■   f) 8970, 8980, 8990, ■, ■

12. Write an increasing number pattern with 4 numbers in each pattern.
    a) starts at 4098 and increases by 1 each time
    b) starts at 3286 and increases by 10 each time
    c) starts at 5709 and increases by 100 each time

13. Find each product.
    a) 12 × 100   c) 6 × 100   e) 3 × 1000   g) 10 × 10
    b) 25 × 100   d) 8 × 1000   f) 4 × 1000   h) 10 × 100

NEL   49

14. Gabe's family bought an entertainment system with 14 one-hundred dollar bills.
    How much did the system cost? Show your work.

15. Amit's mom bought a digital camera with 50 ten-dollar bills.
    How much did the camera cost? Show your work.

16. Round each number to the nearest thousand.
    a) 8245   c) 789   e) 3333   g) 2954
    b) 9079   d) 6378   f) 7690   h) 6193

17. Round each number in Question 16 to the nearest hundred.

18. Round each number in Question 16 to the nearest ten.

19. Estimate each total. Then calculate the actual total.

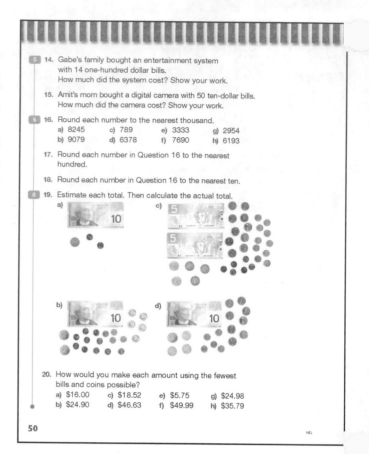

20. How would you make each amount using the fewest bills and coins possible?
    a) $16.00   c) $18.52   e) $5.75   g) $24.98
    b) $24.90   d) $46.63   f) $49.99   h) $35.79

50   NEL

---

7. a) 986 > 953 b) 2234 < 2432 c) 7629 > 983
   d) 10 000 > 1000 e) 9909 < 9990 f) 7685 > 7658
   g) 559 < 5590 h) 1342 < 1351 i) 3980 < 4995

8. a) 693, 7982, 8561, 8642
   b) 653, 3241, 3248, 3379, 9805
   c) 7899, 7982, 7984, 7992
   d) 543, 5070, 5672, 9870, 9930

9. a) For example, 7099, 7909, 9097, 9970
   b) For example, 2448, 2844, 4428, 8244
   c) For example, 1035, 1350, 3510, 5310

10. a) Spanish
    b) Greek
    c) 9020, 7455, 6495, 6345, 3055, 2325

11. a) 70 b) 5000, 5001 c) 8731, 8735
    d) 7682, 8682 e) 983, 1083 f) 9000, 9010

12. a) 4098, 4099, 4100, 4101 b) 3286, 3296, 3306, 3316
    c) 5709, 5809, 5909, 6009

13. a) 1200 b) 2500 c) 600 d) 8000
    e) 3000 f) 4000 g) 100 h) 1000

14. 14 × $100 = $1400

15. 50 × $10 = $500

16. a) 8000 b) 9000 c) 1000 d) 6000
    e) 3000 f) 8000 g) 3000 h) 6000

17. a) 8200 b) 9100 c) 800 d) 6400
    e) 3300 f) 7700 g) 3000 h) 6200

18. a) 8250 b) 9080 c) 790 d) 6380
    e) 3330 f) 7690 g) 2950 h) 6190

19. a) $11.11 b) $15.65 c) $18.20 d) $17.05

20. a) 1 ten dollar bill, 1 five dollar bill, 1 loonie
    b) 1 twenty dollar bill, 2 toonies, 3 quarters, 1 dime, 1 nickel
    c) 1 ten dollar bill, 1 five dollar bill, 1 toonie, 1 loonie, 2 quarters, 2 pennies
    d) 2 twenty dollar bills, 1 five dollar bill, 1 loonie, 2 quarters, 1 dime, 3 pennies
    e) 1 five dollar bill, 3 quarters
    f) 2 twenty dollar bills, 1 five dollar bill, 2 toonies, 3 quarters, 2 dimes, 4 pennies
    g) 1 twenty dollar bill, 2 toonies, 3 quarters, 2 dimes, 3 pennies
    h) 1 twenty dollar bill, 1 ten dollar bill, 1 five dollar bill, 3 quarters, 4 pennies

Problem Bank

Using the Problem Bank

Materials: base ten blocks, play money (bills and coins)

1. Some students may see right away that Ravi has only 1 thousands block and will figure out that they need to model the difference between 2232 and 1 thousands block. They will quickly estimate that the number of available hundreds and ones blocks is not enough to model 1000.

2. The logical answer to this question is any of 1010, 1020, 1030, 1040 and so on up to 1090. However, some tens could be any amount of tens. The answer is any number greater than 1000 ending in a zero.

3. Students will first have to determine what the least 5-digit number is and can do so in many different ways.

4. Students do not have to follow the steps in the order presented when determining the two numbers.

7. Encourage students to make an organized list to create possible 4-digit numbers from the digits provided.

9. b) Students can find the solution in other ways as well. For example, some students may use a table such as the following:

Number of Quarters	Amount of $
4	$1
8	$2
12	$3
16	$4
20	$5

I know that 20 quarters equals $5, and that 8 × 20 = 160, so 8 × $5 = $40.

Encourage students to solve the problem in different ways, asking them to explain their method.

Related Questions to Ask

Ask	Possible Response
About **Question 5:** • Why can you make more 4-digit numbers using the digits 7, 9, 7, and 1 than with 7, 9, 7, and 0? • Can you think of 4 digits that would make more 4-digit numbers than 7, 9, 7, and 1?	• *I can't make any 4-digit numbers starting with 0.* • *Yes, any 4 different digits would make more 4-digit numbers because 7, 9, 7, and 1 uses the same digit twice.*
About **Question 8:** • Why does this question ask what bills and coins *could* Lily have?	• *There is more than one possible answer. All possible answers must include 2 twenty dollar bills, but different sets of 8 coins could be used to make $2.60:* • *2 loonies, 6 dimes* • *2 loonies, 2 quarters, 4 nickels* • *1 toonie, 5 dimes, 2 nickels* *There are more possibilities if students know that there are 50 coins.*

Problem Bank

CHAPTER 2

LESSON

1. Ravi wants to build a model of 2232. He has these blocks. Can Ravi build the model? Use pictures, numbers, and words to explain your answer.

2. A number is represented by 10 hundreds blocks and some tens blocks. What could the number be?

3. Write the number in standard form that is 100 less than the least 5-digit number.

4. Write 2 numbers that match this description. The 1st number is less than the 2nd number. The 1st number has a 4 in the thousands place. The 2nd number has a 4 in the hundreds place.

5. a) Write as many different 4-digit numbers as you can using the digits 7, 9, 7, and 0.
   b) Which of your 4-digit numbers is the greatest? Which of your numbers is the least?

6. There are 100 holes in a ceiling tile. How many tiles would you need to make a total of 1000 holes?

7. 3 towns each have a population that rounds to 8000. Use the digits 2, 3, 7, and 8 to create possible populations for the 3 towns.

8. Lily has $42.60 in her pocket. She has 2 bills and 8 coins. What bills and coins could she have?

9. a) Predict which is worth more, 160 quarters, 480 dimes, or 3999 pennies.
   b) Use a calculator to find the answer.

51

Answers

1. For example, no. The largest number he can model with his blocks is 1225. This number is smaller than 2232. One way he could model 2232 would be using 2 thousands blocks, 2 hundreds blocks, 3 tens blocks, 2 ones blocks

2. For example, 1030

3. 9900

4. For example, 4777 and 5477

5. a) 9770, 9077, 9707, 7970, 7907, 7790, 7709, 7097, 7079
   b) 9770, 7079

6. 10 tiles

7. For example, 7823, 7832, 8237, 8273, 8327, 8372

8. For example, 2 twenty dollar bills, 2 loonies, and 6 dimes

10. a) For example, I predict 160 quarters is worth the most.
   b) 160 × 0.25 = $40.00; 480 × 0.10 = $48.00; 3999 × 0.01 = $39.99; therefore, 480 dimes is worth more.

Chapter Review

Using the Chapter Review

Use these pages to assess students' understanding of the concepts developed in the chapter so far. Refer to the assessment chart on the next page for the details of each question.

Preparation and Planning

Materials	base ten blocks, play money (bills and coins)
Workbook	p. 19, all questions
Masters	• (manipulatives substitute) Base Ten Blocks, Masters Booklet, pp. 33-35 • (manipulatives substitute) Play Money 1, Masters Booklet, p. 27 • (manipulatives substitute) Play Money 2, Masters Booklet, p. 28 • (manipulatives substitute) Play Money 3, Masters Booklet, p. 29 • Chapter 2 Test Pages 1 & 2, pp. 61-62

Students may choose to use base ten blocks to help them solve the questions, whether or not the question suggests they do so. Placing blocks or writing digits directly onto a place value chart may also help those students who have difficulty solving any of the questions.

6. Some students may see right away that any digit greater than 1 placed in the thousands place of the first number will make this number sentence correct. It doesn't matter what digit is placed in the tens place of the second number.

10. Some students may not recognize the multiplicative relationship between 14 g and 140 g immediately. They may want to figure out how many 14 g there are in 140 g and may even use repeated addition. Encourage students to look back at Lesson 5 and then see if they recognize the x 10 relationship.

16. Provide play money for those students who need to use manipulatives to answer these questions.

Journal

Ask students to record in their journals their thoughts now, having completed the chapter, about the chapter goal that they wrote about at the beginning of the chapter. (See Chapter 2 Opener Teacher's Resource page 9.) Then have them compare their responses and reflect on what they have learned.

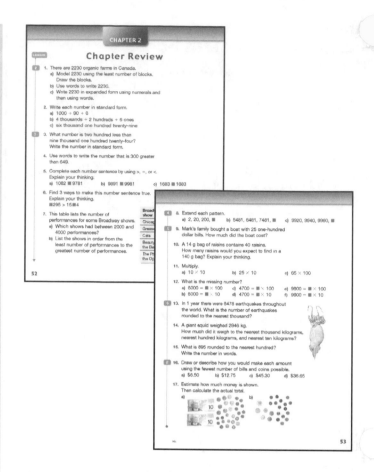

Related Questions to Ask

Ask	Possible Response
About **Question 7:** • The 4-digit numbers in this question all have different digits in the thousands place. Name 5 other 4-digit numbers that would be more difficult to order than these.	• I could name 5 numbers that all had the same digit in the thousands place. • I could name 3 numbers that had the same digit in the thousands and hundreds place and then name 2 other numbers.
About **Question 15:** • Ask students to create a situation for the question.	• It is 895 km to my cousin's house. What is that rounded to the nearest hundred km?
About **Question 16:** • How did you decide which bills and coins to use?	• I knew I had to use the least number of bills and coins, so I started with the largest bill I could. Then I figured out the difference between the amount and the bill and used the next largest bill or coin I could, and so on.

Answers

1. **a)** 2 thousands blocks, 2 hundreds blocks, 3 tens blocks
   b) two thousand two hundred thirty
   c) 2000 + 200 + 30; 2 thousands + 2 hundreds + 3 tens

2. **a)** 1096 **b)** 4206 **c)** 6129

3. 8924

4. nine hundred forty-nine

5. **a)** 1082 < 9781; the thousands digit in 9781 is greater than the thousands digit in 1082
   b) 9891 < 9981; the thousands digits are the same but the hundreds digit in 9981 is greater than the hundreds digit in 9891
   c) 1683 = 1683; the thousands, hundreds, tens, and ones digits are the same for these two numbers

6. For example, 2295 > 1524; 8295 > 1504; 6295 > 1594; any digit greater than 1 must be placed in the thousands place of the first number and any digit can be placed in the tens place of the second number.

7. **a)** Beauty and the Beast and Grease
   b) Chicago, Beauty and the Beast, Grease, The Phantom of the Opera, Cats

8. **a)** 2000 **b)** 8481 **c)** 9980

9. $2500

10. 400; 140 g is 10 × 14 g and 400 raisins is 10 × 40 raisins.

11. **a)** 100 **b)** 250 **c)** 6500

12. **a)** 60 **b)** 600 **c)** 47 **d)** 470 **e)** 99 **f)** 990

13. 6000

14. 3000, 2900, 2950

15. nine hundred

16. **a)** one $5 bill, one loonie, 2 quarters
    b) one $10 bill, one toonie, 3 quarters
    c) two $20 bills, one $5 bill, one quarter, one nickel
    d) one $20 bill, one $10 bill, one $5 bill, one loonie, two quarters, one dime, one nickel

17. **a)** $23.28
    b) $5.06

Assessment of Learning—What to Look for in Student Work...

Assessment Strategy: written question
Understanding Concepts, Communication

Question 1
- There are 2230 organic farms in Canada.
  a) Model 2230 using the least number of blocks. Draw the blocks. (Score 1 point.)
  b) Use words to write 2230. (Score 1 point.)
  c) Write 2230 in expanded form using numerals and then using words. (Score 1 point each for a total of 2.)

Assessment Strategy: written question
Communication

Question 2
- Write each number in standard form.
  a) 1000 + 90 + 6
  b) 4 thousands + 2 hundreds + 6 ones
  c) six thousand one hundred twenty-nine
(Score correct responses out of 3.)

Assessment Strategy: written question
Communication

Question 3
- What number is two hundred less than nine thousand one hundred twenty-four? Write the number in standard form.
(Score correct response out of 1.)

Assessment Strategy: written question
Communication

Question 4
- Use words to write the number that is 300 greater than 649. (Score 1)

Assessment Strategy: written question
Understanding of Concepts

Question 5
• Complete each number sentence by using >, =, or <. Explain your thinking.
 a) 1082 ■ 9781
 b) 9891 ■ 9981
 c) 1683 ■ 1683
(Score 1 point for each ✓ for a total of 6)

Student Name	• number sentence is completed correctly			• shows grade-appropriate understanding			Score out of 6
	a)	b)	c)	a)	b)	c)	
Solange	✓	✓			✓	✓	4

Assessment Strategy: written question
Application of Procedures

Question 6
• Find 3 ways to make this number sentence true. Explain your thinking. ■ 295 > 15 ■ 4
(Score 1 point for each ✓ for a total of 6)

Student Name	• number sentence is completed correctly			• provides complete explanation of thinking			Score out of 6
	a)	b)	c)	a)	b)	c)	
Althea	✓	✓	✓		✓	✓	5

Assessment Strategy: written question
Understanding of Concepts

Question 7
This table lists the number of performances for some Broadway shows.
a) Which shows have between 2000 and 4000 performances?
b) List the shows in order from the least number of performances to the greatest number of performances.

Student Name	• correct response to a) (Score 1)	• Re-ordered list is correct (Score 2)	• Re-ordered list is partially correct (Score 1)	Score out of 3
Brenda	1		1	2

Assessment Strategy: written question
Application of Procedures

Question 8
• Extend each pattern.
a) 2, 20, 200, ■   b) 5481, 6481, 7481, ■   c) 9920, 9940, 9960, ■
(Score correct responses out of 3.)

Assessment Strategy: written question
Application of Procedures

Question 9
• Mark's family bought a boat with 25 one-hundred dollar bills. How much did the boat cost?
(Score correct response out of 1.)

Assessment Strategy: written question
Application of Procedures

Question 10
• A 14 g bag of raisins contains 40 raisins. How many raisins would you expect to find in a 140 g bag? Explain your thinking.

1	2	3	4
Application of Procedures			
• selects an inappropriate procedure for solving the problem	• selects a simple or partially appropriate procedure for solving the problem	• selects an appropriate procedure for solving the problem	• selects the most efficient procedure for solving the problem

Assessment Strategy: written question
Application of Procedures

Question 11
• Multiply. a) 10×10 b) 25×10 c) 65×100
(Score correct response out of 3.)

Assessment Strategy: written question
Application of Procedures

Question 12
• What is the missing number?
  a) $6000 = \blacksquare \times 100$ b) $6000 = \blacksquare \times 10$ c) $4700 = \blacksquare \times 100$ d) $4700 = \blacksquare \times 10$ e) $9900 = \blacksquare \times 100$ f) $9900 = \blacksquare \times 10$
(Score correct response out of 6.)

Assessment Strategy: written question
Understanding of Concepts

Question 13
• In 1 year there were 6478 earthquakes throughout the world. What is the number of earthquakes rounded to the nearest thousand?
(Score correct response out of 1)

Assessment Strategy: written question
Understanding of Concepts

Question 14
• A giant squid weighed 2946 kg. How much did it weigh to the nearest thousand kilograms, nearest hundred kilograms, and nearest ten kilograms?
(Score correct responses out of 3.)

Assessment Strategy: written question
Communication

Question 15
• What is 895 rounded to the nearest hundred? Write the number in words.
(Score correct responses out of 2.)

Assessment Strategy: written question
Understanding of Concepts

Question 16
• Draw or describe how you would make each amount using the fewest number of bills and coins possible.
  a) $6.50 b) $12.75 c) $45.30 d) $36.65

1	2	3	4
• demonstrates a superficial or inaccurate understanding of number concepts involving money amounts	• demonstrates an incomplete understanding of number concepts involving money amounts	• demonstrates grade-appropriate understanding of number concepts involving money amounts	• demonstrates in-depth understanding of number concepts involving money amounts

---

Assessment Strategy: written question
Problem Solving

Question 17
• Estimate how much is shown. Then calculate the actual amount.

Make a Plan

• shows insufficient understanding of the problem and state amounts	• shows partial understanding of the problem and offers estimate	• shows complete understanding of the problem and offers estimate within reasonable range	• shows in-depth understanding of the problem and offers estimate within reasonable range

Carry Out the Plan

• attempts to solve problem but does not arrive at a correct answer	• carries out the plan to some extent and counts money to come up with a partial and/or incorrect solution	• carries out the plan and counts money accurately to solve the problem	• shows flexibility and insight when counting the money by trying and adapting several strategies to solve the problem

Chapter Task

Expectations

4m2 compare and order whole numbers (and decimals) using concrete materials and drawings

4m7 solve problems involving whole numbers (and decimals), and describe and explain the variety of strategies used

4m10 read and write whole numbers to 10 000 in standard (expanded) and written forms

4m12 represent the place value of whole numbers (and decimals from 0.01 to 10 000) using concrete materials, drawings and symbols

4m15 represent and explain number concepts and procedures

4m32 explain their thinking when solving problems involving whole numbers

Use this task as an opportunity for performance assessment, to give you a sense of students' understanding of place value and their ability to use base ten blocks to represent a number. This task requires students to demonstrate their problem solving skills.

Preparation and Planning

Pacing	**10–15 min** Introducing the Chapter Task **30–45 min** Creating a Puzzle
Materials	• base ten blocks • Base 10 overhead manipulatives (optional) • Base 10 stamps (appropriate for students with fine motor difficulties) • Overheads for Chapter 2 Task Master pp. 1 and 2 (optional) • blank overhead sheet (optional) • Yellow pencil crayon for each student (optional)
Enabling Activities	• See Lesson 6. Review the meaning of "population." Discuss population of students' community and nearby communities. Write the numbers on the board.
Nelson Web Site	• Visit www.mathk8.nelson.com and follow the links to *Nelson Mathematics 4*, Chapter 2 to view samples of students' work and assessment support notes.

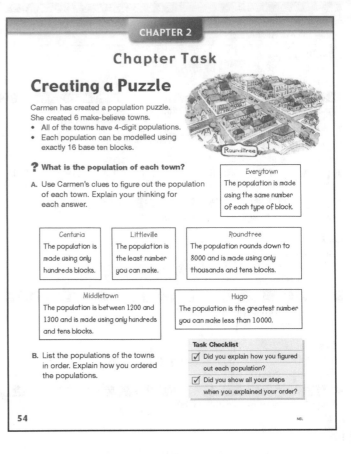

CHAPTER 2

Chapter Task

Creating a Puzzle

Carmen has created a population puzzle. She created 6 make-believe towns.
• All of the towns have 4-digit populations.
• Each population can be modelled using exactly 16 base ten blocks.

? **What is the population of each town?**

A. Use Carmen's clues to figure out the population of each town. Explain your thinking for each answer.

> **Everytown**
> The population is made using the same number of each type of block.

> **Centuria**
> The population is made using only hundreds blocks.

> **Littleville**
> The population is the least number you can make.

> **Roundtree**
> The population rounds down to 8000 and is made using only thousands and tens blocks.

> **Middletown**
> The population is between 1200 and 1300 and is made using only hundreds and tens blocks.

> **Hugo**
> The population is the greatest number you can make less than 10000.

B. List the populations of the towns in order. Explain how you ordered the populations.

Task Checklist
- ✓ Did you explain how you figured out each population?
- ✓ Did you show all your steps when you explained your order?

54

NEL

Introducing the Chapter Task
(Whole Class) ▶ 10–15 min

Review with students the meaning of *population*.

If your community has a population of 4 digits, show how it would be represented using base ten blocks. If your community has a population of more than 4 digits, find an example of a 4-digit population to work with.

Have the students think of ways to describe this population. Share some ideas using mathematical language. (Encourage students to use mathematical vocabulary such as *digits, column, value, greater than,* or *rounds up to*.)

Ask the students how many base ten blocks are used to represent this population. (If the population is 2406, it would use 12 blocks.) Invite students to use the same number of base ten blocks to create a different population (e.g., 4233 also uses 12 blocks). Record populations on the overhead or board. Try to include at least one example that uses more than 9 of one type of base ten block (12 hundreds could be be used to form a population of 1200). Have students compare and order these populations.

Using the Chapter Task ⟩ 30-45 min

Review the names of the towns with students and have them read the directions aloud. If you are using the Chapter 2 Task Master, pp. 63-64, have students highlight the important parts of the directions with a yellow pencil crayon on their copies (e.g., 4-digit, explain in words, draw, 16 base ten blocks. Also highlight the clues for each town. Show where the drawings should be made.)

(If you wish to consider a different performance assessment idea, see Adapting the Task.)

While students are working, observe and/or interview individuals to see how they are interpreting and carrying out the task.

Assessing Students' Work

Use the chart below as a guide for assessing student work. You may wish to have some students explain their work out loud or you may scribe for them. To view samples of students' work at different levels, visit the Nelson Web site, www.mathk8.nelson.com.

Assessment of Learning—What to Look for in Student Work...

Assessment Strategy: observation and product marking
Problem Solving

	1	2	3	4
Problem Solving	Shows insufficient understanding of the problem (i.e., is unable to identify or consider population details)	Shows partial understanding of the problem (i.e., is able to identify and consider some of the population details)	Shows complete understanding of the problem (i.e., is able to identify and consider most of the population details)	Shows in-depth understanding of the problem (i.e., is able to identify and consider all of the population details)
Understanding of Concepts Part A & B	Makes very simple and/or inconsistent observations about the use of base ten blocks to represent and compare 4-digit populations	Makes simple observations about the use of base ten blocks to represent and compare 4-digit populations	Makes appropriate observations about the use of and the relationship between base ten blocks and their value to represent and compare 4-digit populations	Makes insightful observations about the use of and the relationship between base ten blocks and their value to represent and compare 4-digit populations
Application of Procedures Part A	Makes major errors and/or omissions when modelling populations using base ten blocks	Makes several errors and/or omissions when modelling populations using base ten blocks	Makes only a few minor errors and/or omissions when modelling populations using base ten blocks	Makes almost no errors when modelling populations using base ten blocks
Communication Part A & B	Organization of models, numbers and words is minimal and seriously impedes communication Uses very little place value vocabulary to represent or compare populations	Organization of models, numbers and words is limited but does not seriously impede communication Uses a limited range of place value vocabulary to clearly represent or compare some populations	Organization of models, numbers, and words is sufficient to support communication Uses appropriate place value vocabulary to clearly represent and/or compare populations	Organization of models, numbers and words is effective and aids communication Uses a broad range of place value vocabulary to clearly and precisely represent and compare populations

Adapting the Task

There are several ways to adapt the task to suit the needs of your students. For example:

- For Parts A & B, reduce the number of towns for which the student needs to find the population.
- Use the master for Chapter 2 Task Pages 63-64.
- Make up your own clues and criteria.
- Make up a new name town, then write a clue for its population. Solve your problem, explaining how your solution fits the clue.
- Instead of finding the populations of towns, substitute a familiar context for the students (e.g., house or apartment numbers).

Family Newsletter

Dear Parent/Caregiver:

Over the next three weeks, your child will be working with numbers to 10 000. Students will represent numbers such as 4725 in a variety of ways and situations. Relationships among numbers and among digits in numbers will be emphasized as students compare and order numbers, explore number patterns, and develop number sense. Your child will also work with play money as students estimate, count, and write money amounts up to $50.

Throughout this time, you and your child can practise some At-Home activities such as the following:

- Your child can read and write numbers found in newspapers or magazines that are between 1000 and 10 000.
- Your child can relate numbers of distances between places she or he has been or has heard about.
- Your child can research migration facts about other animals and compare them to the monarch butterfly.
- Your child can open a book (with a minimum of several hundred pages) to two different pages and compare the two numbers using clear math language.
- Your child can count out the amount of money needed when you are purchasing items together at a store.
- Your child can look through newspaper or store flyers and count out the bills and coins needed to purchase various items.

You may want to visit the Nelson Web site at **www.mathk8.nelson.com** for more suggestions to help your child learn mathematics and for books that relate children's literature to numbers up to 10 000. Also check the Web site for links to other Web sites that provide online tutorials, math problems, and brainteasers.

If your child is using the *Nelson Mathematics 4 Workbook*, pages 11 to 19 belong to Chapter 2. There is a page of practice questions for each of the 8 lessons in the chapter and a Test Yourself page at the end. If your child requires assistance, you can refer to the At-Home Help section on each Workbook page.

Chapter 2: Mental Math Page 1

LESSON

1   1. How many tens blocks are needed to make these numbers?

     a) 60   **b)** 90   **c)** 100   **d)** 120

     2. How many hundreds blocks are needed to make these numbers?

     a) 500   **b)** 900   **c)** 600   **d)** 1000

2   3. Solve each problem in your head.

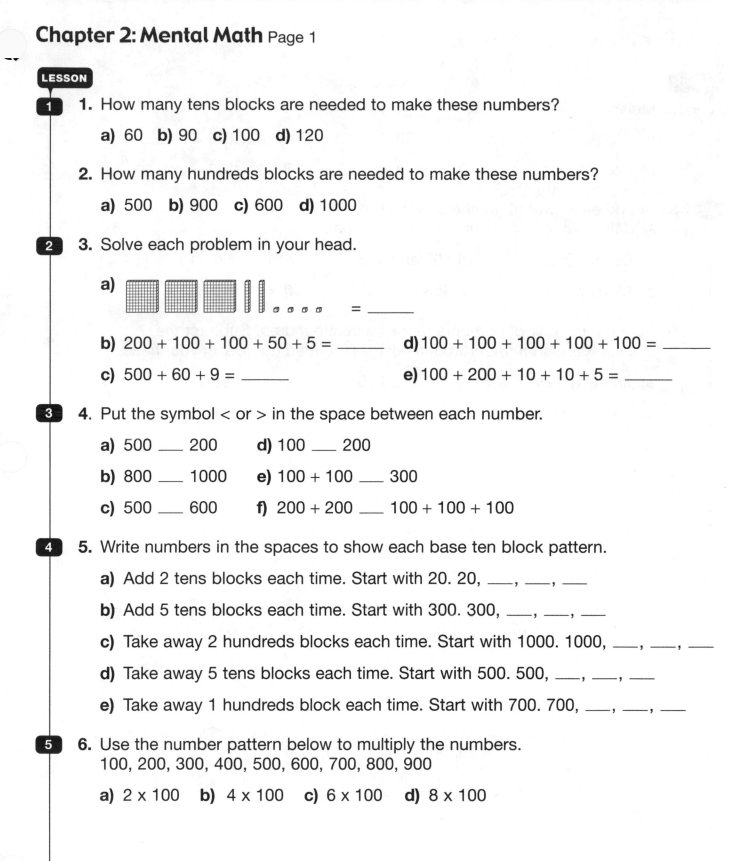

     a) = _____

     b) 200 + 100 + 100 + 50 + 5 = _____   **d)** 100 + 100 + 100 + 100 + 100 = _____

     c) 500 + 60 + 9 = _____   **e)** 100 + 200 + 10 + 10 + 5 = _____

3   4. Put the symbol < or > in the space between each number.

     a) 500 ___ 200   **d)** 100 ___ 200

     b) 800 ___ 1000   **e)** 100 + 100 ___ 300

     c) 500 ___ 600   **f)** 200 + 200 ___ 100 + 100 + 100

4   5. Write numbers in the spaces to show each base ten block pattern.

     a) Add 2 tens blocks each time. Start with 20. 20, ___, ___, ___

     b) Add 5 tens blocks each time. Start with 300. 300, ___, ___, ___

     c) Take away 2 hundreds blocks each time. Start with 1000. 1000, ___, ___, ___

     d) Take away 5 tens blocks each time. Start with 500. 500, ___, ___, ___

     e) Take away 1 hundreds block each time. Start with 700. 700, ___, ___, ___

5   6. Use the number pattern below to multiply the numbers.
     100, 200, 300, 400, 500, 600, 700, 800, 900

     a) 2 x 100   **b)** 4 x 100   **c)** 6 x 100   **d)** 8 x 100

Chapter 2: Mental Math Page 2

LESSON

7. Multiply.

a) 5 x 10 = _____   c) 7 x 100 = _____   e) 15 x 100 = _____

b) 5 x 100 = _____   d) 15 x 10 = _____   f) 10 x 100 = _____

6 | **8.** Round each pair of numbers to the nearest hundred.
Add the two rounded numbers in your head.

a) 98 and 205   c) 105 and 478   e) 124 and 113

b) 99 and 98   d) 458 and 295   f) 444 and 333

9. Round each pair of numbers to the nearest hundred. Subtract the
smaller rounded number from the larger rounded number in your head.

a) 398 and 205   c) 479 and 205   e) 324 and 113

b) 299 and 98   d) 454 and 259   f) 898 and 388

7 | **10.** Put the numbers in order from least to greatest. Add the numbers in
your head.

a) 50, 20, 30, 10   c) 50, 30, 40, 10

b) 100, 500, 200, 300   d) 500, 100, 300, 400

8 | **11.** Add these money amounts in your head.

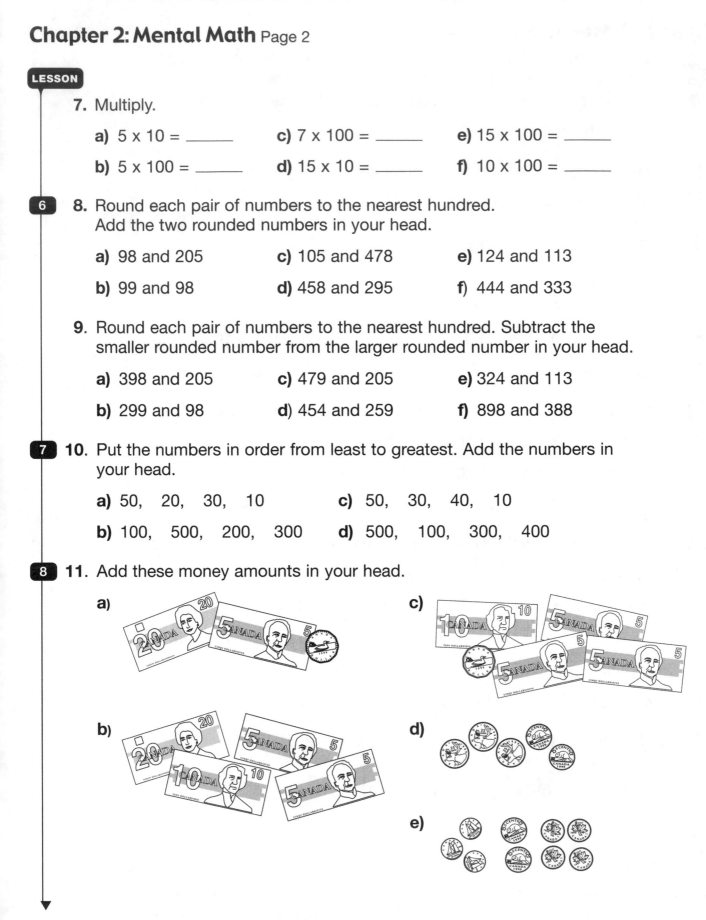

a)

c)

b)

d)

e)

Chapter 2 Test Page 1

1. Kagna lives 2840 km from Canada's capital city, Ottawa, Ontario.

   a) Model 2840 using the least number of blocks.
      Draw the blocks.

   b) Use words to write 2840.

   c) Write 2840 in expanded form using numbers and then in expanded form using words.

2. Write each number in standard form.

   a) 3000 + 200 + 40 + 8

   b) 8 thousands + 5 tens + 6 ones

   c) five thousand forty-nine

3. Complete each number sentence by using >, =, or <.
   Explain your thinking.

   a) 2093 _____ 8681   b) 4950 _____ 5490   c) 1119 _____ 1118

4. Extend each pattern.

   a) 4, 40, 400, _____   c) 9020, 9030, 9040, _____

   b) 7371, 6371, 5371, _____   d) 1594, 1596, 1598, _____

5. Multiply.

   a) 88 x 10 = _____   c) 10 x 100 = _____

   b) 6 x 1000 = _____   d) 1000 x 10 = _____

Chapter 2 Test Page 1

6. This table lists the distances that some animals migrate.

Animal	Distance (km)
Arctic Tern	2880
Green Turtle	2527
Humpback Whale	2200
Bald Eagle	1920
Peregrine Falcon	5770

a) What is the migration distance of the Green Turtle rounded to the nearest hundred? What is the distance rounded to the nearest ten?

b) Explain why the migration distances of the Arctic Tern and the Green Turtle are both 3000 when rounded to the nearest thousand.

c) Write the migration distances in order from the least distance to the farthest distance.

7. Estimate the total. Then calculate the actual total.

1 twenty-dollar bill, 1 ten-dollar bill, 2 five-dollar bills, 4 quarters, 9 dimes

8. Draw and describe how you would you make this amount using the fewest bills and coins possible.

$42.85

Chapter 2 Task Page 1

Creating a Puzzle

STUDENT BOOK PAGE 54

Carmen created 6 make-believe towns.

- All of the towns have 4-digit populations.
- Each population can be modelled using exactly 16 base ten blocks.
- Each town has a clue so you can figure out the population.

? What is the population of each town?

A. Use Carmen's clues below to figure out the population of each town.

Everytown

Clue: The population is made using the same number of each type of block.

Draw the population using 16 base ten blocks.	Explain how you got your answer.

Centuria

Clue: The population is made using only hundreds blocks.

Draw the population using 16 base ten blocks.	Explain how you got your answer.

Littleville

Clue: The population is the least number you can make.

Draw the population using 16 base ten blocks.	Explain how you got your answer.

Chapter 2 Task Page 2

Creating a Puzzle

STUDENT BOOK PAGE 54

Roundtree

Clue: The population rounds down to 8000 and is made using only thousands and tens blocks.

Draw the population using 16 base ten blocks.	Explain how you got your answer.

Middletown

Clue: The population is between 1200 and 1300 and is made using only hundreds and tens blocks.

Draw the population using 16 base ten blocks.	Explain how you got your answer.

Hugo

Clue: The population is the greatest number you can make less than 10 000.

Draw the population using 16 base ten blocks.	Explain how you got your answer.

B. List the populations of the towns in order.

_____ _____ _____ _____ _____ _____

Explain how you ordered the populations.

Name: _____ Date: _____

Scaffolding for Getting Started Activity

A. a) Use base ten blocks to model 326 like this.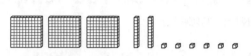

    b) Look at your model.
How do you know 326 is greater than 300?
How do you know 326 is less than 400?

B. Look at your model of 326.
Suppose you traded all the tens
blocks for ones blocks.

Draw the new model for 326.

C. This model of 326 has 11 blocks.

Suppose you traded blocks until it
had 20 blocks.
Draw the new model for 326.

D. Make the greatest number you can with 11 blocks.
Choose at least 1 hundreds block, 1 tens block and 1 ones block.
Draw your blocks.
What is the number?

E. Make the least number you can with 11 blocks.
Choose at least 1 hundreds block, 1 tens block and 1 ones block.
Draw your blocks.
What is the number?

Scaffolding for Do You Remember?

STUDENT BOOK PAGE 29

1. a) 169 = 1 hundreds + 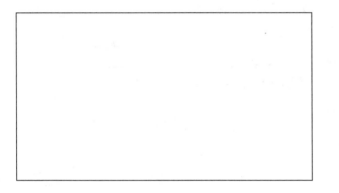 tens + 9 ones

   b) 961 = ■ hundreds + 6 tens + ■ ones

   c) 320 = ■ hundreds + ■ tens + ■ ones

   d) 507 = ■ hundreds + ■ tens + ■ ones

2. Circle the number that is greater.

   a) 639 or 714   **b)** 495 or 475   **c)** 306 or 360

3. Order the numbers from least to greatest.

   a) 384, 389, 364, 368   364, _____, _____, 389

   b) 870, 780, 817, 728   _____, 780, _____, _____,

4. a) You can make $4.50 using 4 loonies and 5 dimes.
   Make $4.50 two other ways.
   Draw or describe your coins.

   b) You can make $9.75 using 9 loonies, 7 dimes, and 5 pennies.
   Make $9.75 two other ways.
   Draw or describe your coins.

Scaffolding for Lesson 3, Question 5
STUDENT BOOK PAGE 35

5. This table shows how far it is from Vancouver to 6 different cities.

City	Distance from Vancouver (km)
Whitehorse, Yukon	2700
Toronto, Ontario	4500
Montreal, Quebec	4800
Moncton, New Brunswick	5825
Calgary, Alberta	1050
St John's, Newfoundland	7675

a) Which city is closest to Vancouver? _____
How do you know?

_____

_____

b) Which city is farthest from Vancouver? _____
How do you know?

_____

_____

c) Which cities are between 3000 km and 6000 km from Vancouver?

3000 km _____ _____ _____ 6000 km

d) Rewrite the table so the cities are in order from farthest from Vancouver to closest.

City	Distance from Vancouver (km)	
		farthest from Vancouver
Montreal, Quebec	4800	
		closest to Vancouver

Name: _____   Date: _____

Scaffolding for Lesson 6, Question 4

STUDENT BOOK PAGE 43

4. This table shows the population of 6 places.

Place	Population
Fergus	8884
Pelee	283
Kincardine	2954
Mount Forest	4580
Petrolia	4908
Gananoque	5210

a) The population of Fergus is 8884.
Show where 8884 would be on this number line.

```
|----+----+----+----+----+----+----+----+----+----|
8000                                            9000
```

Would you round 8884 to 8000 or to 9000? _____

b) The population of Pelee is 283. Show where 283 would be on this number line.

```
|----+----+----+----+----+----+----+----+----+----|
200                                              300
```

Would you round 283 to 200 or to 300? _____
Show where 283 would be on this number line.

```
|----+----+----+----+----+----+----+----+----+----|
280                                              290
```

Would you round 283 to 280 or to 290? _____

c) Look at the table at the top of the page.
What place has a population of about 3000? _____

d) Explain why 4580, 4908, and 5210 all round to 5000.

Place	Population	Rounded to the Nearest Thousand
Mount Forest	4580	5000
Petrolia	4908	5000
Gananoque	5210	5000

_____

_____

_____

Chapter 2: Answers

Problem of the Week, p. 3

1. For example, students could work with a partner and use a stopwatch or watch with a second hand to time how long it takes their partner to count to 100. They can then multiply that number by 100.

2. The answer will vary according to the size of print in telephone book. A telephone book from a large city has about 10 000 names on 1 1/4 pages.

3. For example, 8114.

Mental Math Master, pp. 59–60

1. **a)** 6   **b)** 9   **c)** 10   **d)** 12
2. **a)** 5   **b)** 9   **c)** 6   **d)** 10
3. **a)** 324 **b)** 455 **c)** 569   **d)** 500   **e)** 325
4. **a)** >   **b)** <   **c)** <
      d) <   **e)** <   **f)** >
5. **a)** 40, 60, 80
      b) 350, 400, 450
      c) 800, 600, 400
      d) 450, 400, 350
      e) 600, 500, 400
6. **a)** 200 **b)** 400 **c)** 600   **d)** 800
7. **a)** 50   **b)** 500 **c)** 700   **d)** 150   **e)** 1500   **f)** 1000
8. **a)** 100 + 200 = 300
      b) 100 + 100 = 200
      c) 100 + 500 = 600
      d) 500 + 300 = 800
      e) 100 + 100 = 200
      f) 400 + 300 = 700

9. **a)** 400 – 200 = 200
      b) 300 – 100 = 200
      c) 500 – 200 = 300
      d) 500 – 300 = 200
      e) 300 – 100 = 200
      f) 900 – 400 = 500
10. **a)** 10 + 20 + 30 + 50 = 110
       b) 100 + 200 + 300 + 500 = 1100
       c) 10 + 30 + 40 + 50 = 130
       d) 100 + 300 + 400 + 500 = 1300
11. **a)** $26.00
       b) $40.00
       c) $26.00
       d) $0.85
       e) $0.44

Chapter 2 Test, pp. 61–62

1. **a)**

b) two thousand eight hundred forty

c) 2000 + 800 + 40; 2 thousands + 8 hundreds + 4 tens

2. **a)** 3248   **b)** 8056   **c)** 5049
3. **a)** <   **b)** <   **c)** >
4. **a)** 4000 **b)** 4371   **c)** 9050 **d)** 1600
5. **a)** 880   **b)** 6000 **c)** 1000 **d)** 10 000
6. **a)** 2500; 2530
      b) For example, 2880 rounded to the nearest 1000 is 3000 and 2527 rounded to the nearest 1000 is also 3000.
      c) 1920, 2200, 2527, 2880, 5770
7. $31.90   41.90
8.

Chapter Task, pp. 63–64

A. Everytown: 4444

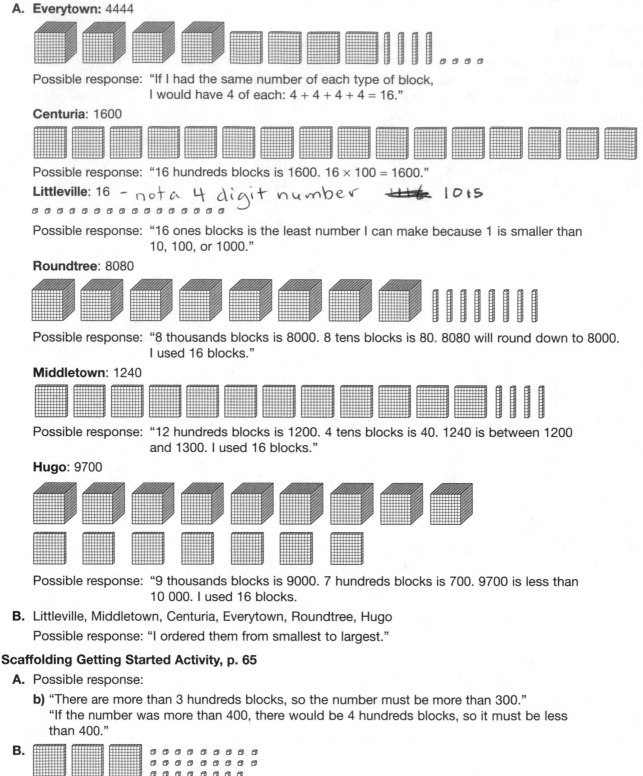

Possible response: "If I had the same number of each type of block, I would have 4 of each: 4 + 4 + 4 + 4 = 16."

Centuria: 1600

Possible response: "16 hundreds blocks is 1600. 16 × 100 = 1600."

Littleville: 16 – *not a 4 digit number* ~~16~~ 1015

Possible response: "16 ones blocks is the least number I can make because 1 is smaller than 10, 100, or 1000."

Roundtree: 8080

Possible response: "8 thousands blocks is 8000. 8 tens blocks is 80. 8080 will round down to 8000. I used 16 blocks."

Middletown: 1240

Possible response: "12 hundreds blocks is 1200. 4 tens blocks is 40. 1240 is between 1200 and 1300. I used 16 blocks."

Hugo: 9700

Possible response: "9 thousands blocks is 9000. 7 hundreds blocks is 700. 9700 is less than 10 000. I used 16 blocks.

B. Littleville, Middletown, Centuria, Everytown, Roundtree, Hugo

Possible response: "I ordered them from smallest to largest."

Scaffolding Getting Started Activity, p. 65

A. Possible response:

b) "There are more than 3 hundreds blocks, so the number must be more than 300."
"If the number was more than 400, there would be 4 hundreds blocks, so it must be less than 400."

B.

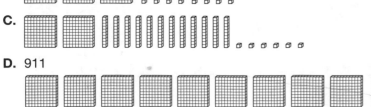

C.

D. 911

E. 119

Scaffolding for Do You Remember, p. 66

1. **a)** 6   **b)** 9, 1   **c)** 3, 2, 0   **d)** 5, 0, 7
2. **a)** 714   **b)** 495   **c)** 360
3. **a)** 368, 384   **b)** 728, 817, 870
4. **a)** For example, 4 loonies and 2 quarters
       For example, 2 toonies and 10 nickels
   b) For example, 9 loonies and 3 quarters
       For example, 9 loonies and 75 pennies

Scaffolding for Lesson 3, Question 5, p. 67

a) Calgary, Alberta
   It is 1050 km away. The other cities are more than 1500 km away.

b) St. John's, Newfoundland
   It is 7675 km away. The other cities are less than 7675 away.

c) Toronto, Montreal, Moncton

d)

City	Distance from Vancouver (km)
St. John's, Newfoundland	7675
Moncton, New Brunswick	5825
Montreal, Quebec	4800
Toronto, Ontario	4500
Whitehorse, Yukon	2700
Calgary, Alberta	1050

Scaffolding for Lesson 6, Question 4, p. 68

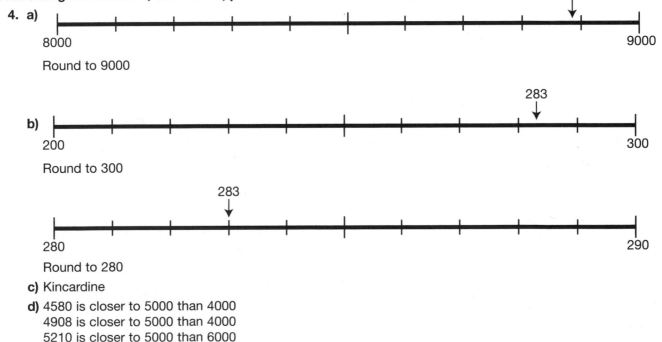

4. **a)**

8884

8000   9000

Round to 9000

b)

283

200   300

Round to 300

283

280   290

Round to 280

c) Kincardine

d) 4580 is closer to 5000 than 4000
   4908 is closer to 5000 than 4000
   5210 is closer to 5000 than 6000